Just for Boys!
Reading Comprehension

Grades 3-6

Written by Nat Reed
Illustrated by Tom Riddolls

ISBN 978-1-55035-813-1
Copyright 2007
Revised May 2008

All Rights Reserved * Printed in Canada

Published in the United States by:
On The Mark Press
3909 Witmer Road PMB 175
Niagara Falls, New York
14305
www.onthemarkpress.com

Published in Canada by:
S&S Learning Materials
15 Dairy Avenue
Napanee, Ontario
K7R 1M4
www.sslearning.com

At A Glance

Learning Expectations	Grade 3 Fiction	Grade 3 Non-fiction	Grade 4 Fiction	Grade 4 Non-fiction	Grade 5 Fiction	Grade 5 Non-fiction	Grade 6 Fiction	Grade 6 Non-fiction
Vocabulary, Word Usage & Grammar								
• Identify word meanings	•	•	•	•	•	•	•	•
• Antonyms/synonyms/compound words/idioms		•	•				•	•
• Dictionary and thesaurus skills	•	•	•	•		•		•
• Writing complete sentences	•	•	•	•	•	•	•	•
Reading Comprehension								
• Identify and describe main text elements	•	•	•	•	•	•	•	•
• Understand words in context	•	•	•	•	•	•	•	•
• Summarize main elements and provide supporting details	•	•	•	•	•	•	•	•
• Identify and describe character traits and relationships between characters	•	•	•	•	•	•	•	•
Reasoning and Critical Thinking								
• Analyze and evaluate text elements	•	•	•	•	•	•	•	•
• Point of view of a character/person	•	•	•	•	•	•	•	•
• Compare and contrast setting or characters/persons	•	•	•	•	•	•	•	•
• Analyze character/people traits and behaviors	•	•	•	•	•	•	•	•
• Identify and describe cause & effect	•	•	•	•	•	•	•	•
• Express opinions, provide evidence from text	•	•	•	•	•	•	•	•
• Evaluate evidence	•	•	•	•	•	•	•	•
• Creative writing/design	•	•	•	•	•			•
• Predict future outcomes	•	•	•		•			•
• Relate text to personal experiences	•	•	•	•	•	•	•	
• Research skills	•	•	•	•	•	•	•	•

Table of Contents

Teacher Assessment Rubric

Student's Name: _____

Criteria	Level 1	Level 2	Level 3	Level 4
Comprehension	Responses demonstrate a **limited** understanding of important information in the passage.	Responses demonstrate a **basic** understanding of important information in the passage.	Responses demonstrate a **good** understanding of important information in the passage.	Responses demonstrate a **thorough** understanding of important information in the passage.
Oral reading	Reads aloud word by word.	May ignore punctuation when reading aloud.	Reads at **varying** rates depending on purpose and encouragement.	Reads aloud **fluently** and effortlessly.
Ability to summarize what has been read	**Limited** summarization of events, main characters, and setting.	Summarizes **most** events, most of main characters, and setting.	Summarizes main events, main characters, and setting with **good** accuracy.	Accurately and **completely** summarizes main events in correct sequence, the main characters, and setting.
Reasoning	**Seldom** makes sound judgments and draws effective conclusions from material.	**Inconsistent** in making sound judgments and drawing effective conclusions from material.	**Fairly consistent** in making sound judgments and drawing effective conclusions from material.	**Consistently** makes sound judgments and draws effective conclusions from material.
Understanding form and style	**Limited** identification of various forms of writing (e.g., poetry, short story, newspaper article) and describing their key features.	**Fair** success at identification of various forms of writing (e.g., poetry, short story, newspaper article) and describing their key features.	**Good** identification of various forms of writing (e.g., poetry, short story, newspaper article) and describing their key features.	Demonstrates **thorough** understanding of various forms of writing (e.g., poetry, short story, newspaper article) and their key features.
Extending beyond text	Responses **do not** make extensions beyond text to other texts and relevant personal experiences.	Responses demonstrate a **little** extension beyond text, but references are general rather than specific.	Responses demonstrate **good** extension beyond text both to other texts and personal experiences.	Responses demonstrate **considerable** evidence of extension beyond text to other texts and personal experiences.

Student Self-Assessment Rubric

Name: _____

Put a check mark in the box that best describes your performance. Then, add your points to determine your total score.

Expectations	My Performance				
	Always (4 points)	Frequently (3 points)	Sometimes (2 points)	Seldom (1 point)	My Points
✔ I was focused and stayed on task.					
✔ My answers are thoughtful and show consistent effort.					
✔ I checked meanings of difficult words/ideas.					
✔ I used all the resources available to me to answer questions.					
✔ I used correct punctuation and sentence structure in my writing.					
✔ I proofread my work for spelling, grammar, and clarity.					
✔ I included my own experiences in my responses whenever possible.					
✔ I know what I do well.					
✔ I know what I need to improve.					

Total Points: _____

Read Aloud Observation Form

Student's Name: _____

This evaluation tool is intended for teachers to use one-on-one with students to assess reading strengths and difficulties. Reading fluency is one of the literacy skills needed for comprehension.

Observation Criteria	Too Fast	Too Slow	Appropriate
Pace of Reading			

Observation Criteria	Several Major Mistakes/Omissions	Several Minor Mistakes/Omissions	Few Mistakes/Omissions
Accuracy			

Observable Pattern: _____

Observation Criteria	No Expression	Little Expression	Appropriate Expression
Expression			

Observation Criteria	Few Pauses for Periods/Commas	Some Pausing for Periods/Commas	Consistent Pausing for Periods/Commas
Attention to Punctuation			

Observation Criteria	Few Strategies to Attack New Words	Some Strategies to Attack New Words	Several Strategies to Attack New Words
Decoding			

Strategies Used: _____

Teacher Suggestions

This resource can be used in a variety of ways:

1. The student booklet focuses on a variety of fiction and non-fiction passages. Each of these sections contains the following activities:

   a) Before you read the passage (reasoning and critical thinking skills; dictionary and thesaurus skills);
   b) While you read the passage (comprehension and higher–thinking questions);
   c) After you read the passage (reading comprehension skills; extension activities).

2. Students may read the passage at their own speed and then select, or be assigned, a variety of questions and activities.

3. **Bulletin Board and Interest Center Ideas:** Themes might include pirates, Will Smith, Jackie Chan, snowmobiling, skateboarding, the duck-billed platypus, the solar system, and monster trucks.

4. **Pre-Reading Activities:** This unit may also be used in conjunction with themes of self-esteem, heroes, personal accomplishments, persevering through new and uncomfortable experiences, fairy tales, the wilderness, and holidays (i.e. Hanukkah).

5. **Independent Reading Approach:** Students who are able to work independently may attempt to complete the assignments in a self-directed manner. Initially these students should participate in the pre-reading activities with the rest of the class. Students should familiarize themselves with the reproducible student booklet. Completed worksheets should be submitted so that the teacher can note how quickly and accurately the students are working. Students may be brought together periodically to discuss issues introduced in a specific reading passage.

6. **Fine Art Activities:** Students may integrate such topics as monster trucks, designing a skateboard park, drawing a map of a deserted treasure island, or creating a poster advertising Will Smith or Jackie Chan's latest movie.

7. Encourage the students to keep a reading log in which they record their readings each day and their thoughts about the passage.

Before Reading

Backyard Sleepover

1. Either from your imagination or your own experience, describe why sleeping out in someone's backyard might be an exciting thing to do.

_____

_____

2. List three items you would be sure to take on a backyard sleepover.

- _____

- _____

- _____

3. Other than someone's backyard, where else might be a good place to spend a night in the outdoors?

_____

_____

4. Find the meaning for the following words. Use a dictionary if necessary.

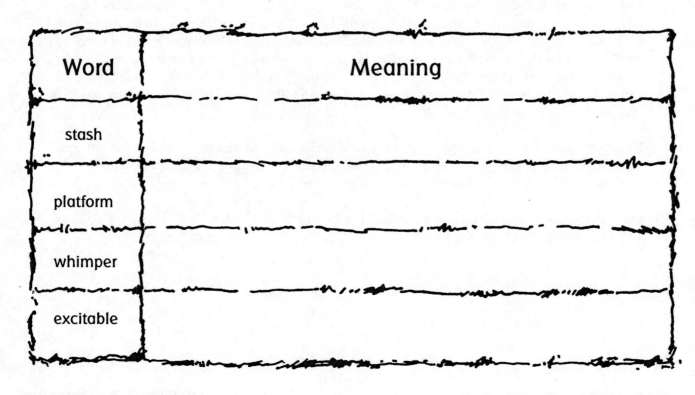

Word	Meaning
stash	
platform	
whimper	
excitable	

Backyard Sleepover

I thought that spending the summer at my cousin Caleb's place would be boring, but it turned out to be pretty exciting after all. Caleb lives in a big, old house in the city, with a huge backyard. In the middle of the yard is a maple tree, where we spent the first week building a treehouse. It wasn't all that much, just a platform, with walls that went up to our knees, and a big flat piece of tin that we used for a roof.

Once the treehouse was finished, we decided to invite Chi-chi, Caleb's friend over to spend the night. Chi-chi was about the same age as Caleb and me, but was a lot shorter and really excitable.

As soon as it was dark we collected our sleeping bags and a stash of snacks, then climbed up into the treehouse. It was a clear, warm night, with a big white moon hanging in the summer sky.

For the first hour or so everything went really well. We lay there under the stars, finishing up our snacks and telling ghost stories. It was the perfect night for a camp-out. We could even hear an old owl hooting off in the distance.

It was then we heard something really creepy – something that sounded like a cat moving slowly up the tree. Scratch . . . scratch . . . scratch.

"What's that?" Chi-chi whispers.

"Sounds like something's coming up the ladder," Jack says.

Chi-chi pulls out his flashlight and shines it over toward the ladder.

Then I swear I could hear this heavy breathing coming from down below.

Chi-chi starts to whimper just like a little kid. "It's a ghost!" he whispers. "Let's get out of here."

> How do you think the boys are feeling right now?

Now I don't believe in ghosts, but I could see that even Caleb looked a little rattled. "It must be my dog, Ralph," Caleb says. He then crawls over to the side of the treehouse and peers down the ladder. "I can't see him, but it must be him."

After that, for the longest time we kept hearing those scratching and breathing noises. Caleb would yell, "Ralph – go home!" But the noises kept up. Finally our eyes started getting heavy and Chi-chi began to snore.

All of a sudden Caleb sits bolt-upright in his sleeping bag. Even in the dark I could see that his eyes were bugged right out.

"What's the matter?" I ask. Even Chi-chi is wide awake.

"Our dog," Jack says. "I just remembered. My brother took him on a camping trip. He's gone for the week." We were quiet for a minute, then Chi-chi says in a really soft voice, "What was that noise then?"

Caleb and I just looked at each other. What was that noise?

 # Backyard Sleepover

This story is an example of a **cliffhanger** – where the ending of the story leaves the reader hanging.

1. Explain what you think the scratching noise was.

2. Why couldn't it have been Caleb's dog, Ralph?

3. Describe what you think was going through the boys' minds when they heard the scratching on the tree.

4. Describe Chi-chi's personality.

5. Why do you think the boys chose Chi-chi to join them for the sleepover?

6. How do you think the boys might have improved their treehouse when they were building it? Try to think of at least two ways.

   -
   -

7. What else might the boys have done to find out what was making the noises?

8. On a sheet of paper, describe what might happen next after the story ends.

Name:_____

sidehill gouger

1. There are many unusual animals. What do you think is the most unusual animal you have ever heard about? Describe it.

_____

_____

_____

2. Do you know someone who is really good at telling stories? What do you think makes a person good at this?

_____

_____

_____

3. Paul Bunyan and Pecos Bill are just two characters made famous by the tellers of tall tales. Do some investigation to find out what a tall tale is, and report on two important characteristics that make a tall tale.

_____

_____

_____

4. Draw a line from the word in the **Column A** to its definition in **Column B**.

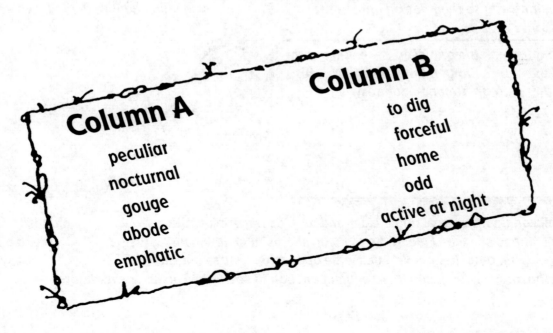

Column A

peculiar

nocturnal

gouge

abode

emphatic

Column B

to dig

forceful

home

odd

active at night

sidehill gouger

"**Y**ou know," the old man said, grinning down at his grandson. "The woods around here are chock-full of the most unusual, fascinating critters, and one of the most peculiar is the sidehill gouger."

"The sidehill gouger?" his grandson echoed. "I've never heard of such an animal."

"Well, that's because you're from the city," the old man said. "And they're a mysterious little varmint too, you almost never hear of them. Another thing, too, is the fact that they're nocturnal – they only come out at night. And they're fast – quick as a greased lightning bolt – naturally with their legs built the way they are – they'd have to be fast!"

"How's that?" the boy asked. "Are they like a rabbit?"

The old man gave a good-natured snort. "Not likely, although they do look a lot like them. I'd say they're more like a groundhog – at least from a distance. You see the sidehill gouger gets its name on account of it living on the sides of steep hills where it gouges out its dens. In fact it's on account of their peculiar abode that these critters are so unusual-looking. Now picture this if you will, on one side of its body the sidehill gouger has one long set of legs, and on the opposite side – a short pair. That way it can move about on the sides of steep hills."

His grandson's mouth dropped open. "Get out of here!"

The old man nodded. "I can tell you another thing too, there's left-handed sidehill gougers and right-handed sidehill gougers. They probably developed that way so they don't all run in the same direction on the hills where they live."

> What do you think the grandson is thinking at this point in the story? Do you think he believes his grandfather's story? Defend your answer.

He picked up his mug of apple cider and took a long drink while his grandson stared at him in stunned silence. Finally the old man set his mug down and gave his head a nod. "Sidehill gougers, boy. Keep your eyes wide open when you're out there in the wilds because who knows, you just might be lucky enough to see one. You just never know."

Name:_____

 **After Reading**

sidehill gouger

1. Where does the Sidehill Gouger live?

_____

2. Describe in your own words how the Sidehill Gouger got to be the way it is.

_____

_____

_____

3. Explain what these unusual expressions from the story mean:

chock-full _____

critters _____

varmint _____

peculiar abode _____

4. The author uses the simile, "quick as a greased lightning bolt". Using your imagination, think of another simile (a comparison using like or as) to describe the gouger's speed.

_____

5. Complete the following comparison chart. You may need to do a little research.

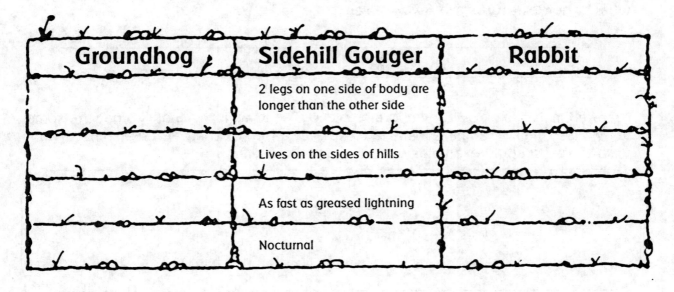

Groundhog	Sidehill Gouger	Rabbit
	2 legs on one side of body are longer than the other side	
	Lives on the sides of hills	
	As fast as greased lightning	
	Nocturnal	

Name:_____

Before Reading platypus meets the big bad wolf

1. Research important facts about the duck-billed platypus and report on its appearance, habitat, diet and enemies.

   _____

   _____

   _____

   _____

2. Which fairy tale features the **big bad wolf**? Describe characteristics about his personality. Why do you think the writers of the fairy tales often made the bad character a wolf?

3. Think of other villains from fairy tales (you may wish to do a little research or discuss some possibilities with a couple of other students). Other than wolves, what other creatures are favorite fairy tale bad guys?

   _____

   _____

4. Many animals are not strong enough to win a fight against a wolf. What are some ways these weaker animals manage to not get eaten by their fierce enemy? (You may wish to use specific examples to back up your answers.)

Platypus meets the big bad wolf

D.B. Platypus was a rather strange-looking creature. In his little part of the world, however, the other animals were quite used to seeing him waddle about near the river. One character, however, was not used to seeing D.B., and that was Cecil Wolf, or Big Bad, as he preferred to be called. You see, Cecil had just moved into the neighborhood on the opposite side of the forest. Cecil had never in his life seen anything like D.B. Platypus, and so he stopped right there on the pathway and stared rudely at his fellow traveler. He moved around the strange-looking animal in a slow circle. "What on earth are you?" he finally asked. "Your feet are webbed like a frog; you've got a bill like a duck, and a broad, flat tail like a beaver."

Now D.B. was no dummy. He'd been warned about wolves and how they'd eat just bout anything. "My name is D.B. Platypus," he said, "You must be new to the neighborhood."

"Why, I'm Big Bad," Cecil, said, licking his chops as he studied D.B.'s round portly sides. "I'm the most ferocious creature this side of the great beyond." The wolf's tongue lolled hungrily from his mouth. Great greedy drops of saliva dripped onto the ground before him.

What might be going through D.B.'s mind at this moment? Defend your answer.

D.B. shifted his pudgy body awkwardly, making sure he was always turned toward the hungry wolf. "I suppose you're wondering how I got to look like this," he said with a sad look. "Before moving here I used to live next to a large nuclear plant on the other side of the mountain. Nuclear waste was dumped into the streams around where we lived, and as a result everyone in our family for the past several generations have turned out looking like this."

"You're a mutant," the wolf gasped, backing up a step.

"Mutant makes us sound like we're freaks," D.B. objected.

The wolf retreated another couple of feet. "Well," he said, beginning to stammer. "It certainly has been a pleasure to meet you, Mr. D.B. If everyone on this side of the forest is as friendly as you are, I shall really feel at home here." With that the wolf turned and fled down the path, quickly disappearing into the distance.

From then on, D.B., and all of the other platypuses living on that side of the forest, were never again bothered by Cecil or any of his hungry family.

Name:_____

platypus meets the big bad wolf

1. Describe the clever strategy that D.B. uses to outsmart Cecil.

2. Do you think it is a good idea to tell a lie to help get someone out of trouble? Be sure to support your answer.

3. What do you think of Big Bad's real name – Cecil? Is this a good name for a wolf? Why or why not?

4. What is a mutant?

5. How does the expression, "better safe than sorry" describe Cecil's attitude at the end of this story?

Name:_____

Before Reading

FROM PRINCE TO ULTRASTAR

1. What does it take to become a movie star?

2. Do you think Will Smith meets these points?

4. Define the word charisma. Do you think that Will Smith has charisma? Defend your answer.

3. Do you think it would be difficult for a singer to be a successful actor? Defend your answer.

5. Match the word on the left with its correct meaning.

a) perform	character
b) audition	do
c) nominate	grow
d) personality	let down
e) disappoint	try out
f) expand	put forward

Will Smith's broad smile is a familiar sight to millions of television and movie fans all over the world. Will was born in West Philadelphia, the second oldest of four children. When he was still quite young, he got the nickname Prince because he was so good at charming his way out of trouble.

Will attended Philadelphia's famous Overbrook High School whose graduates also include Wilt Chamberlain, Hal Lear, and DeeDee Sharp.

How can a good high school education help a person achieve success?

Will's movie career really took off. In 1996 he had another huge hit, "Independence Day", in which he battled aliens. Since then he has starred in blockbusters such as "Ali" and "Hitch".

How was Will prepared for his career as a movie actor?

Will is married to Jada Pinkett Smith, whom he met on the set of his television series. Jada was there to audition for the role of his girlfriend. The couple have one son, Jaden, who was born in 1998 and a daughter, Willow, born in 2000.

Will has already received many honors. He won Grammy Awards for his songs, "Summertime" and "Parents

WILL SMITH

Will always loved music, and it wasn't long after he met Jeff Townes at a party that the two began performing together as DJ Jazzy Jeff and the Fresh Prince. The duo quickly became a very popular music act. As the group became more successful, Will was asked about acting in a sitcom based on his life, but set in California. Both Will and the people at NBC loved the idea and in 1990 the television series, "The Fresh Prince of Bel-Air" was born. The series lasted for six, very popular years and during this time Will was able to expand his acting career by appearing in several successful movies. With the action picture, "Bad Boys",

Just Don't Understand", and was also the first hip-hop artist to be nominated for an Academy Award.

Will's favorite big screen hero is Harrison Ford. He claims that his biggest disappointment was refusing the role of Neo in "The Matrix".

Many people (including former President Clinton) look to Will as a positive role model for young people. In January 2005, he was voted into the Top 15 Greatest Teen Idols by "TV Guide" magazine. With Will's musical and acting talents, and his friendly personality, he should enjoy a successful career for many years to come.

Name:_____

WILL SMITH

1. Pedict Will Smith's future in acting and singing. If you were his agent, what roles and activities would you have him concentrate on during the next five years?

2. Research: What other movies has Will Smith appeared in?

3. This biography mentions a number of other successful people who attended Overbrook High School. Choose one of the people mentioned and research three interesting facts about him/her.

_____

_____

_____

4. If you were to meet Will Smith and have a conversation with him, what three questions would you like to ask him?

_____

_____

_____

5. Action movies are very popular for many years. Some of Hollywood's most successful action stars have included Errol Flynn, Harrison Ford, and Bruce Willis. Why do you think Will Smith has been such a success as an action hero?

_____

_____

_____

Name:_____

Making The Team

1. Either from your own experiences or imagination, describe what it would be like to try out for a sports team.

_____

_____

_____

_____

2. What thoughts might go through a player's mind who **makes** a team.

_____

_____

_____

3. How might a player who doesn't make a team feel? (Be specific about his feelings).

4. Besides being good at the sport being tried out for, what other things might a coach look for in his players?

_____

_____

_____

5. What might you say to a person who doesn't make a team to help him feel better about himself?

Making The Team

Football, basketball, soccer – does making a team depend only on one's athletic ability?

Most coaches, no matter what the sport, will admit that being a good athlete is only a part of what they look for in a player. There are many other factors that are also considered that you might want to think about when trying out for a team.

To begin with, coaches look to see how much drive and desire a player has. Is the player satisfied with his skill level, or is he looking to improve his play at each and every practice?

Secondly, is the player a one man show or is he a team player? The coach is always looking for players that will fit into his game plan. Players are expected to sacrifice their own personal stats for the good of the team. It is also important to coaches that a player gets along well with his teammates. (No one likes playing with a Hollywood.)

How does the old saying, "winning isn't everything", fit with what has been said so far?

Believe it or not, good sportsmanship is also important to most coaches. A player who loses control of his emotions during the game may be penalized by the referee or umpire and cause his team to lose.

Another important factor is whether or not the player is coachable. A good coach can break down each part of a player's game and teach him what to do in order to improve his skills. Will the player listen? Will he trust his coach and put the effort into improving, or will he decide that he knows better than the coach? Perhaps the player doesn't feel the hard work and sacrifice that needs to go into

improving his game is worth it.

As well, don't be afraid to ask the coach if he has any advice to give you about how you might make the team. It may be that the coach is looking for a player with one special skill, and by practicing hard in that one area, you can be successful (e.g., a punter on a football team).

The more competitive a team is, of course, the more difficult it will be to make the roster, yet even the best teams and the most serious coaches look at more than just how athletic a player is. And remember, when there isn't much difference in ability between you and several other players, these other factors may be the deciding factor between who gets to play – and who doesn't.

Name:_____

Making The Team

1. Why do you think that most coaches value desire to improve?

_____

_____

2. Give an example of when putting your team above your own personal glory is important.

_____

_____

3. In your own words, summarize one of the suggestions made in this article.

_____

_____

4. What does it mean when a player is described as coachable?

_____

_____

5. Name one other thing that might be important to a coach that isn't mentioned in this article?

6. If you tried out for a team and didn't make it, what might you do to make the team the next time?

_____

_____

Volume 29 Issue 3

July 2006

the Eyewitness News

Chesterville Daily, 33325 Jumper Lane, Chesterville, MI 35489   (268) 354-3049

Before Reading

By The Solski Group

1. **Investigate: check out a copy of the** *Guinness Book of World Records.* **Describe a record that you find most interesting or unusual.**

   _____

   _____

   _____

2. **If you were thinking of trying to break a world record, what would it be?**

   _____

   _____

   _____

3. **Someone might try to cheat when attempting to break a world record. How do you think the people at Guinness might try to prevent people from lying or cheating?**

   _____

   _____

   _____

   _____

4. **A compound word is a word made up of two smaller words (e.g., outhouse). List four more examples of compound words.**

   _____

   _____

   _____

   _____

What's Inside

News... pg 2-5

Editorial... pg 6-8

Entertainment... pg 9-13

Features... pg 14-25

Sports... pg 26-30

Volume 29 Issue 3

July, 2010

the Eyewitness News

Chesterville Daily, 33325 Jumper Lane, Chesterville, MI 35489   (268) 354-3049

Local Boy Sets World Record

By Alfred Guinness

Donnie Lapointe, a 12 year old boy from nearby Selwyn Corners, established a world record yesterday on his modified BMX bike. Donnie is a grade 7 student at General Custer Public School, and has been an avid BMX rider since grade 3.

What is incredible about Donnie's accomplishment is that he and his best friend, Jack Walpoole, began their quest for world recognition only a few weeks ago.

> Using your imagination and what you know of BMX bikes, what world record might Donnie and Jack have broken?

"When we got out for the summer holidays, Jack and I were thinking we should do something different – something to make the summer stand out." Donnie told our reporter. "So we went through the *Guinness Book of Records* looking for something we could do on our bikes that we'd be recognized for."

What a record it turned out to be! Just three weeks ago these two young daredevils got to work. First, they were able to talk Ralph Emberley, owner of Chesterville Lumber Yard, into donating enough lumber to build a 25 foot long ramp at the bottom of Bunker Hill. There, Donnie, Jack and a number of their friends went to work putting together their plywood covered ramp.

"The next part was the toughest," Donnie admitted. "We had to collect 20 outhouses." Twenty outhouses! Believe it or not, the boys' plan involved jumping over 20 honest-to-goodness outhouses – how they managed to collect so many of these little buildings we may never know.

How did the boys come up with this particular challenge? "We noticed that the record book talked about the highest indoor jump, and the highest air achieved, and even things like the longest backflip, but it didn't mention jumping over outhouses," Donnie told us.

"The people at Guinness were a little suspicious at first," Donnie confessed, "But after we told them the details of our plans, they finally agreed. They told us to download the proper forms and make sure we had the media and a local sheriff present when we attempted the jump." The boys' quest, however, began with failure. "On my first jump, I crashed into the last outhouse and had to go get cleaned up," Donnie told us. But then success! A jump totaling over 60 feet in length and more than 15 feet in height, that cleared all 20 outhouses.

Congratulations, boys. You've done your hometown proud. **Donnie Lapointe – World's Champion Outhouse Jumper.**

Volume 29 Issue 3

July 2006

the Eyewitness News

Chesterville Daily, 33325 Jumper Lane, Chesterville, MI 35489   (268) 354-3049

After Reading

1. What prompted Donnie and Jack to try to break a world record?

   _____
   _____
   _____

2. Describe the record that the boys were attempting to set.

   _____
   _____
   _____

3. What happened on Donnie's first attempt?

   _____
   _____
   _____
   _____

4. Describe in as much detail as possible what it must have looked like when Donnie made his record-setting jump.

   _____
   _____
   _____
   _____

5. Why do you think Donnie's hometown was so proud of his world record?

   _____
   _____
   _____

Next challenge – cars

1. Drawing from your own experiences or your imagination, name two advantages of having an older sister, and two disadvantages.

- •   •
- •   •

2. Do you think it would be better to be the oldest or the youngest in a family? Explain your answer.

_____

_____

3. Describe how you might feel if your class was taking a trip to the local high school. Why might you feel this way?

_____

_____

4. Use each of the following words in a sentence which shows its correct meaning.

orientation: _____

_____

appreciate: _____

_____

saunter: _____

_____

session: _____

_____

guidance: _____

_____

cafeteria: _____

_____

counselor: _____

_____

Big Sister

Having an older sister has always been the biggest pain in the world. Although Kaitlyn is only two years older than me, you'd think she was my junior mom, the way she bosses me around – and my friends too, for that matter.

Whenever I complain to my mom she just says, "Someday you'll appreciate having an older sister, Corey." And she was right – sort of, anyway.

On Friday all the grade eight students in our school were invited over to the high school for an afternoon – to meet the teachers, and sit in on a couple of classes. It sounded like fun.

A big yellow school bus took us all over there right after lunch. After a session with the principal in the cafeteria, a guidance counselor took us on a tour of the school. That's when the trouble started.

> Predict what this crisis might be.

On the way to the gym I suddenly had to go to the bathroom in the worst possible way, so when we passed the boys' washroom, I nipped inside. I was only there for a minute, but when I got back out into the hallway, my class was long gone!

I was standing there in the hallway when who should come sauntering by with that smug look on her face – but Kaitlyn.

"What's the matter, little brother?" she asks.

"Can't find my class," I said with a shrug.

She rolls her eyes, then says to me in a tired voice. "Better follow me." With that she just heads off down the hallway and across the school we go.

How she knew where my class was at that moment, I don't know. But before I knew it we were standing outside the auto shop class. Kaitlyn pokes her head into the room and waves me forward. "They're gathered around that old car," she whispers. "Everybody has their backs to us – if you hurry, they'll never notice you were gone." Without further ado she winks at me and heads off down the hall.

I slip into the classroom, and sure enough no one even notices when I sidle up beside Justin. He looks at me and whispers, "What happened to you?"

I just shrugged. "Took a little detour."

And so ever since last Friday I have come to appreciate my older sister just a little bit more, even though she still goes out of her way to bug me.

Name:_____

2. How might Corey have handled his crisis so that he wasn't separated from his class?

1. What Crisis at the high school led to Corey's problem?

_____

_____

3. What three words might describe Corey's feelings when he realized he couldn't find his class?

4. Why do you think Corey's sister helped him out when he couldn't find his class?

_____

_____

5. Explain how Corey came to have a better appreciation of his sister through the events in this story.

_____

_____

6. Kaitlyn seems to be a very confident girl. Find proof of this from the story.

Before Reading

Captured by Aliens

1. Describe a time when you got into trouble at home or at school. What did you do to get into trouble? What were the consequences?

_____

_____

_____

_____

2. Have you ever made up a story to get yourself out of trouble? If so, tell about this incident (or make one up). What might be the disadvantage to this strategy?

_____

_____

_____

3. If creatures from another planet really do exist, describe what you think they might look like.

•

•

•

•

4. Look up the word gullible in the dictionary. Would you describe yourself as gullible? Why or why not?

_____

_____

_____

_____

Captured by Aliens

Dear Mom and Dad:

I know you must be worried about me – ever since I disappeared this morning after breakfast. When you got mad at me and told me to take the garbage out, these strange creatures kidnapped me, sucking me into their space craft (which looks like a giant ketchup bottle). You may find this hard to believe, but now they have allowed me to write **one letter**, to let you know where I am.

> Why do you think someone would write a letter to his parents to convince them that he had been captured by aliens?

The aliens aren't little green men like you might think. Although they are green, they're actually quite tall, and real skinny. In fact they look like big, ugly frogs. The aliens have told me they're from the planet Xerxes, which is in a far-off galaxy.

You can imagine how scared I was when I first got kidnapped. The aliens just sucked me up into their spaceship, strapped me to a table and started asking me all kinds of questions about Earth: the kind of weapons we have, and how big our armies are. I was really scared, but I kept my mouth shut – even when they tortured me by sticking toothpicks under my fingernails. (I'll show you the marks!) I sure didn't want to be responsible for my own planet being captured. After about a half-hour, they got really angry and said if I didn't start answering their questions they would probe my brain for the next twenty years.

I know you must be sad to lose your only son – especially when you were so mean to him this morning. He didn't mean to break the car window or smash that big hole in the living room wall. I heard the aliens say that they will be blasting off into space this afternoon, so if I don't escape by then, I probably won't see you for at least twenty years. I just wish I could see my wonderful family one more time, and know that if I did manage to escape, you would be glad to see me too, and probably even forget about grounding me until next Sunday.

I am begging and begging these ugly green frogs to let me go. If they do, I will be so glad to see you that I'll never misbehave again.

Your loving son,
Caleb

Name:_____

Captured by Aliens

1. Write a letter to your parents or a friend describing an imaginary encounter you have had with an alien. Be sure to describe how you happened to meet them and include a description of the aliens.

```
_____
_____
_____
_____
_____
_____
_____
_____
_____
```

2. What information were the aliens trying to get from Caleb?

_____

_____

3. What two things had Caleb done to upset his parents?

 -

 -

4. Do you think Caleb was really captured by aliens? Defend your answer.

_____

_____

_____

1. What is the most unusual person you have ever met? Include a description of this character.

3. The Dingledorf poet describes a particularly bad day in his life. Describe a particularly bad day that you had to endure.

2. The dingledorf is an unusual three-syllable animal name. Can you think of other unusual three-syllable animal names? You may have to brainstorm this one with one or two classmates.

4. What is a mastadon?

The dingledorf

I met one day a dingledorf,
When I was traveling to
A country town not far from here
Who taught me everything he knew.
It wasn't much,
It took not long,
For he was such a dork.
All that he knew
Could fit into
The pocket of a stock.

Is there such an animal as a dingledorf? On what do you base your answer?

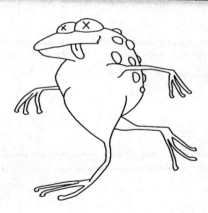

I met one day a three-toed toad,
He hopped a little funny.
He kept a-tripping o'er his feet
And landing on his tummy.
I think he'd had,
Too much to drink,
That was a little naughty!
I meant no ill,
but I slipped and fell,
And squashed his little body.

I met one day a camel herd,
Out back beyond the town,
They were grazing in my uncle's field,
Those two-humped mastodons.
I wonder just,
How quick they are,
I'll take one for a race.
But when I jumped,
Up on his humps,
He spit right in my face!

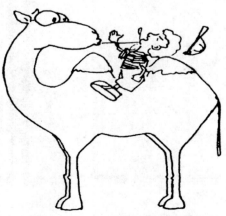

Name:_____

The dingledorf

1. Using your imagination, describe in detail, the appearance of a dingledorf.

2. From the poem, match each animal with the correct description.

dingledorf	clumsy
toad	rude
camel	not very clever

3. Which of the following idioms do you think would best describe the dingledorf?
   (Underline the correct response.)

   a) smart as a whip   c) dumb as a post

   b) sly as a fox   d) sharp as a tack

4. Investigate: The poem's toad had only three toes on each foot. How many toes does a normal toad have?

5. Describe the toad's fate in this poem.

6. Investigate: Under what circumstances do camels spit at people?

Name:_____

tear it up

Before Reading

1. Name three things that someone buying an All Terrain Vehicle (ATV) would think are important?

-

-

-

2. For what activities might an ATV be used?

_____

_____

_____

_____

3. If you were to create an advertisement for an ATV, what information would you be sure to include?

_____

_____

_____

_____

4. The ATV can be a dangerous vehicle to operate. List three safety rules you would recommend to anyone driving one.

-

-

-

tear it up

The New Stallion 22XC Turbo-Powered ATV

The Stallion 22XC All-Terrain Vehicle is especially designed for off-road use. It is capable of traveling on grass, sand, gravel, mud and even light snow. Its powerful 6hp engine is smooth and quiet and the machine's low center of gravity makes the Stallion easy to manoeuver. The Stallion 22XC is inexpensive to maintain and operate, and even uses regular gasoline. It is a popular vehicle for hunting and fishing trips.

Special Features

- Transmission automatically shifts with terrain changes
- Adjustable handlebar clamps accommodate different sized riders
- Studded tires for better grip
- Convenient hand brake
- Steel fenders and mud flaps protect the rider and bike
- Heavy duty roller chain and a big steel chain guard

World ATV Racing Champ, Max Million, has called the **Stallion 22XC** the most powerful, best-equipped ATV he has ever ridden.

Purchase for $1,500.00
Lease for as low as $200 per month

tear it up
After Reading

1. **List six of the Stallion 22XC's specs or selling points.**

   _____

   _____

   _____

   _____

   _____

   _____

2. **Why do you think including Max Million's endorsement might be effective in selling more Stallion 22XCs?**

   _____

   _____

   _____

3. **Look again at Max Million's statement. Is he saying that the Stallion 22XC really is the most powerful, best-equipped ATV you can buy? Explain your answer.**

   _____

   _____

   _____

4. **Supposing there is no tax on the purchase of a Stallion 22XC, and no interest charges on the lease. How many months would it take to pay off the ATV according to the ad?**

   _____

5. **Design your own poster advertising one of the following products: a bicycle, skateboard, car, truck, or motorcycle. Using the advertisement for the Stallion 22XC as an example, you should include a picture of the product and as much important information as you can. Remember your goal is to get people to want to buy the product.**

Name:_____

Before Reading JACKIE CHAN

Note: If you are unfamiliar with Jackie Chan, you might want to check him out on the Internet first.

1. What do you like best about Jackie Chan's movies?

2. Think of a way that one of his movies might be improved.

3. Why do you think Jackie Chan is such a popular actor?

4. Summarize the plot of your favorite Jackie Chan movie.

_____

_____

_____

_____

_____

_____

_____

_____

_____

_____

_____

5. What is a stunt actor?

The movie star that millions know and love as Jackie Chan, was named Kong-sang Chan when he was born. His name means born in Hong Kong. Chan began his acting career at the young age of six when (while a student at the China Drama Academy) he was offered a role as a stunt actor. With his enthusiasm and growing talent, Jackie soon began taking on larger and more important roles. He rose to the position of stunt coordinator, and then film director. He even worked as a stunt coordinator with the martial arts legend, Bruce Lee.

The death of Bruce Lee was an important turning point in Jackie's life, for the world began looking for an actor to replace Lee. Jackie decided that rather than try to copy Lee, he would develop his own style of filmmaking. Jackie was a great fan of the early comedians, Buster Keaton, Charlie Chaplin, and Harold Lloyd, and this is evident in many of his movies. One of Jackie's first films, "Shi di chu ma" set the tone for many of his future movies, combining slapstick humor with high-energy martial arts action.

Jackie performs all of his own stunts, which has resulted in many injuries. He has broke his nose (three times), his ankle, most of his fingers, both cheekbones and his skull. His movies also often contain scenes in which he is tortured or is subjected to a lot of physical activity. In his action scenes, Jackie's punches and kicks actually connect with their targets. To prevent injury, his co-stars wear special padding on their feet and body. Not only does he do his own stunts, he expects the other actors and actresses in his movies to do their own as well. Jackie's stunt team is highly trained and is expected to perform the way Jackie does, matching him move for move, speed for speed. For this reason, many actors have trouble keeping up with him.

JACKIE CHAN

Why do you think Jackie insists on all the actors in his movies performing their own stunts?

In 1976 Jackie underwent plastic surgery to re-shape his eyelids. This gave him a more "western" appearance.

Jackie has appeared in a number of successful movies including "Rush Hour", "Rush Hour 2", and "Shanghai Noon". For his role in "Rush Hour 2", Jackie received more than $15,000,000.

Jackie is married and has two children, and lives in America.

Name:_____

JACKIE CHAN

1. What has been the physical result of Jackie performing his own stunts?

_____

_____

2. Why did Jackie have cosmetic surgery? Do you think that this was necessary? Explain your reasons?

_____

_____

_____

3. In replacing Bruce Lee as the world's greatest kung fu star, what important thing did Jackie add to his movies that weren't present in Lee's?

4. Do you think this was a good idea? Explain your answer.

_____

_____

_____

5. What kind of movies did Charlie Chaplin, Buster Keaton, and Harold Lloyd appear in?

THE UNKNOWN DWARF PLANET

Before Reading

Test your knowledge of the planets in our solar system:

1. All of the planets orbit around what celestial object?_____

2. Until 2003, it was believed there were _____ planets in the solar system.

3. Which planet has been known as the red planet? _____

4. Which planet is thought to be most similar to Earth? _____

5. The hottest planet is _____.

6. Pluto is now called a _____-_____.

7. How many years does it take for the Earth to orbit the Sun? _____

8. The Earth is the only planet in our solar system with a moon.
   T   or   F

9. The Earth's moon has an influence on the ocean's tides.
   T   or   F

10. Write a definition in your own words for each of these words and then find out what the word really means. How many definitions did you guess correctly?

    astronomer: _____

    debate: _____

    orbit: _____

    variety: _____

    debris: _____

    dwarf planet: _____

    researcher: _____

    recently: _____

    telescope: _____

THE UNKNOWN DWARF PLANET

In October 2003, astronomers in California first photographed a separate, planet-like object at the edge of our solar system. The object looked like a ring of icy debris and was labeled UB313 by the scientists. UB313 is the farthest known object in the solar system, even further than Sedna, a planetoid discovered a few years ago. Since 2003, scientists have been observing this object with a variety of powerful telescopes, gathering more and more information about its size and its elements.

UB313 is located about nine billion miles away from the sun – 97 times farther than the Earth. It is also three times farther from the Sun than Pluto, which until recently was believed to be the farthest planet from the Sun in our solar system. UB313's orbit is not as regular as the other planets; and it's 560 year cycle around the sun is not a circular path. The planets orbit the sun like a giant flat frisbee, whereas this object's orbit is on a 45 degree tilt.

While researchers say they aren't sure of UB313's actual size, they are quite sure that it is bigger than Pluto, which had been considered a planet since its discovery in 1930.

Why do you think scientists don't know how large UB313 is?

There is a great debate among astronomers whether UB313 should actually be called a planet. It is similar to Pluto which is also different from the other eight planets. Pluto, for instance, is only one-fifth the size of our moon. Scientists decided in 2006 that both Pluto and UB313 should be classified as a part of the icy debris on the outer reaches of the solar system; they invented a new term to describe these objects--dwarf planets. Pluto is no longer a planet! Like Sedna and UB313, Pluto is a dwarf planet. Scientists think there are more dwarf planets out there, but they don't know how many. These scientists say that if UB313 is called a planet, then a couple of dozen other objects in the far reaches of the solar system should be too.

Planet	Diameter	Distance from Sun
Mercury	3,050 miles (4,880 km)	36 million miles (58 million km)
Venus	7,588 miles (12,140 km)	68 million miles (108 million km)
Earth	7,973 miles (12,756 km)	94 million miles (150 million km)
Mars	4,242 miles (6,787 km)	143 million miles (228 million km)
Jupiter	89,250 miles (142,800 km)	486 million miles (778 million km)
Saturn	75,413 miles (120,660 km)	0.88 billion miles (1.4 billion km)
Uranus	31,949 miles (51,118 km)	1.8 billion miles (2.9 billion km)
Neptune	30,955 miles (49,528 km)	2.8 billion miles (4.5 billion km)

Name:_____

THE UNKNOWN DWARF PLANET

1. Do you think UB313 and Pluto should be classified as planets? Defend your answer.

2. Why do some scientists believe that UB313 and Pluto should not be called planets?

3. a) How large is Pluto in comparison to our moon?

b) In what year was the planet Pluto discovered?

c) How large do astronomers think UB313 is?

4. According to the chart, the largest planet is _____. The smallest planet is _____. The two planets which are closest together are _____ and _____. The planet closest to the size of Neptune is _____. The planet which is 94 million miles (150 million kilometers) from the sun is called _____ .

Treasure Map

1. List five things you're reminded of when you think of pirates.

   _____
   _____
   _____
   _____
   _____

2. Why do you think so many pirates buried their treasures?

   _____
   _____

3. List three items that might be included in a pirate's buried treasure.

   _____
   _____
   _____

4. Where do you think a person might find an ancient pirate's treasure map today? Be as specific as possible. (e.g., in a desk drawer at an antique shop)

   _____
   _____

5. What is the "Bermuda Triangle"?

   _____
   _____

6. On a separate sheet of paper, make up your own map of a pirate's treasure. Be sure to include enough detail to make it interesting. When you are finished reading "Treasure Map", go back to your map and see if there is anything you would like to change or add to it.

Treasure Map

West Catalina Island lies a few leagues northwest of the Bahamas in the very center of the dreaded Bermuda Triangle. The island is long, narrow, and uninhabited. It takes no more than a half-day to walk from north to south. Like most of the islands in the region it is also very beautiful, with towering palm trees and white, sandy beaches.

It is on this desolate spit of land that in the spring of 1774, Captain Peg-leg McQueeg chose to bury the plunder he stole from the British ship, King George. What follows are the Captain's own directions, which, if followed to a T, will lead a treasure-hunter to the exact spot of the stolen booty. The clues are in Captain McQueeg's own words, so you may have to do some interpreting.

Ahoy, mateys! Back in '74, after a fierce battle lasting three days, the lads and I boarded the HMS King George and put to the plank everyone aboard. It 'twas a great ship bound from the New World and laden with gold, jewellery and all manner of treasure. So filled was its hold that it took more than two days to haul it aboard the Maggie Mae. As soon as we were done, we scuttled the King George and did a little pipe dance as she disappeared beneath the briny deep.

> **Think of three words that would describe the personality of a typical pirate.**

What a crew I had with me on that trip! Between the sinking of the George and our next sighting of land, we went through two mutinies and a fierce outbreak of the plague. When we finally did reach West Catalina Island (as bare and barren as it was), there was only me, the mate and three lonely sailors left of a souls. The five of us knew it wasn't with such a vast treasure, so we treasure and come back later with

crew that had once numbered 40 possible to defend a ship laden down decided there and then to bury the some trusted mateys.

That was our plan when lonely island. But by the time at Kingston harbor, I alone knaves in Kingston immediately years have passed since and I fear my days are truly though, is that I might die and treasure with me to my grave. So for few, yet valuable pages, over to you – my last

we hid the treasure there on that our poor Maggie Mae docked survived – and the scurvy threw me in the brig. Two long they put me in this foul prison, numbered. My greatest fear, take the secret of the buried that reason I am turning these trusted friend on earth. Now

don't betray me, Padre, or I'll crawl into your dreams at night and haunt your every waking moment until the day you die!

Now listen up and we'll see how good you are at following the directions of an old sea dog! Give an ear now, lad.

Treasure Map

Mid-point up the western coast of West Catalina Island lies a shallow bay that I named Letitia Cove, after my third wife. There, where the beach throw wide, lies a large rock which can be seen from the the rock at exactly one hour past sunrise and face due east. on, matey. Just don't stand there looking like you just teeth! I'll tell you why in a minute.

is but a stone's shoreline. Go to Now get a move swallowed your false

Forty paces from the rock toward the rising sun palm trees side by side (pray they haven't been blown monsoon). When the sun has risen two hours beyond the horizon, a perfect shadow is cast by the two trees. Follow in the direction of the shadows another 30 paces. There you will come to the edge of a large swamp, but your journey is not yet o'er. Make yourself comfortable, scurvy land-lubber, but watch for them crocodiles – they're hungrier than a starving man at a pie-maker's picnic!

stands two large over by a

Two or three hours before sundown a wind will begin to blow. It always comes from the same direction at this time of day. Turn your face to the wind and walk in a straight line until you reach the ocean's edge, then backtrack fifteen paces. There you must dig. Dig like you've never dug before, because the water comes into the hole almost as fast as one can dig – so you must be quick or get nothing but salt sea water!

Why do you think Captain McQueeg chose this method of directing the Padre to the treasure instead of drawing him a map?

As tall as a man, as deep as a small boat is wide, that's the size of the hole you must prepare.

Yet should you uncover my treasure before I die – beware! It is my treasure, and should you take it out from under my nose, I will follow you to the ends of the earth to get it back. Good luck, my little friend, you'll surely be needing it!

Name:_____

Treasure Map

1. Investigate: Research three interesting facts about one of the following famous real-life pirates: Francis Drake, William Kidd, Anne Bonny, Jean Laffite, Henry Morgan or Edward Teach (Blackbeard).

   _____
   _____
   _____
   _____

2. Investigate: The "skull and crossbones" or "jolly roger" are names for the famous pirate flag. Research a couple of interesting facts about this flag (e.g., its origin, purpose).

   _____
   _____
   _____

3. Captain McQueeg appears to be a real odd character. What impressed you the most about him?

   _____
   _____

4. What circumstances led McQueeg to bury the treasure?

   _____
   _____

5. Why was he now revealing its location?

   _____
   _____

Name:_____

A RISKY RIDE

1. Match each word in Column A with its correct meaning in Column B.

Column A   Column B

a) accelerator   1. clear shield to protect driver

b) treads   2. instrument indicating speed

c) slush   3. large belt driving different machines

d) snowmobile   4. long, flat runners

e) speedometer   5. "gas pedal"

f) windscreen   6. small winter vehicle

g) skiis   7. mixture of snow, ice, and water

2. What dangers might a snowmobiler face?

3. If you were going snowmobiling in the wilderness, how would you
   dress (be as specific as possible) and what survival items would you
   take with you?

_____

_____

4. Investigate: Do some research and choose a model of snowmobile.
   What company makes it? Describe the specs of the snowmobile you
   investigated. How do the advertisers make owning one seem desirable?

_____

_____

A RISKY RIDE

A lot of kids probably wouldn't think so, but I've always thought I'm really lucky to live in the north. For one thing, I can go snowmobiling and that's what I enjoy doing more than anything else.

A few weeks ago I was out for a ride on my snowmobile when I arrived at the shores of a river miles from my home. I've always been cautious about crossing rivers on my snowmobile, because even a foot of ice can be covered with a thick layer of slush. Slush can mean getting hopelessly bogged down, and out in the middle of nowhere, that would be an absolute nightmare!

"If I go fast enough, I should be okay." I said to myself, giving my Yamaha a reassuring pat.

Taking a deep breath, I gunned the motor - pressing the accelerator all the way to the handlebar. The sled screamed out from the shoreline, jerking me back in my seat and launching me forward. I caught air for what seemed like forever before I landed with a crash several sled-lengths out on the ice. Immediately I began hightailing it across the river at top speed.

Describe a similar risky experience you've had (e.g., in a boat or car, riding your bike, skateboarding).

After 100 yards or so I checked back over my shoulder to see if there was any tell-tales signs of slush. None! So far, so good.

In seconds I had the Yamaha up to 60 miles an hour in snow that was only a few inches deep. But by the time I was half-way to the other side, I noticed the sled begin to labor a bit. I took a quick look behind. A long, yellow trail was now visible behind me. Slush! My heart almost stopped. How deep was it? If it wasn't too deep I might still have a chance, otherwise the watery sludge would begin sticking to the treads and gradually slow me down until I was hopelessly mired, miles from help. I checked the speedometer. Forty miles per hour. If I waited any longer to turn back, it would be too late!

In your own words, describe the dilemma of this snowmobiler.

A RISKY RIDE

Through the windscreen I could see the shoreline approaching – the length of a huge swimming pool away.

I squeezed that last bit of juice from the engine, leaning up over the windscreen, but the sled continued to slow down. I wasn't going to make it! My only hope would be if the slush eased up toward shore.

I was now only a stone's throw from two big birch trees dead ahead . . . I glanced at the speedometer. Twenty-eight miles per hour.

I was almost there!

Behind me water was now shooting out from my treads, throwing up a great stream high into the air.

Suddenly a wave of panic seemed to rush through me. What if I got the snowmobile stuck way out here in the middle of nowhere? Within minutes the treads would be frozen solid in the ice and I would never get it free by myself. I would then have to hike several long miles through the wilderness in the freezing cold. I wasn't even sure I could make it.

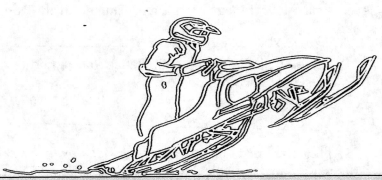

Would it be a good idea for the driver to try to turn back at this point? Why or why not?

Ten miles per hour . . . the motor roared laboriously as it crawled the last few feet through the deep slush and up onto the riverbank. I breathed a huge sigh of relief as the sled rode up the loose powder snow on the shore.

"We made it!"

I jumped from my machine and yanked off my helmet. But even as I did, a sudden thought leapt into my mind. I looked back at the long yellow snowmobile tracks trailing out behind me. "I won't be able to return this way," I said out loud. "And this river stretches for miles in either direction, so how on earth am I ever going to get home!"

Name:_____

A RISKY RIDE

1. This story ends with the main character in a very desperate situation. Describe how he managed to get himself into such a crisis.

2. What possible solution to this problem do you think he might come up with?

    _____

    _____

    _____

3. What makes slush so dangerous to a snowmobiler?

4. Why was speed so important in this situation?

    _____

    _____

    _____

5. Why should a snowmobiler always tell someone at home the route he/she is taking before setting out?

Name:_____

1. Describe what you think it would feel like on your first day at a new school.

2. When does teasing stop being fun and begin to be cruel?

3. What is it about some kids that makes it fun for others to tease them?

4. What effect do you think teasing might have on someone?

_____

_____

5. Why do you think it is difficult to tell one of your friends to stop teasing someone else?

The New Kid

Lester Brubaker was probably the nerdiest kid I'd ever seen in my life. To start with, he barely came up to my chin, and he had these great, clunky glasses, red hair and freckles. . . . and that crow's nest of his! It stood straight up from the back of his head like it had a mind of its own!

When he first walked into our classroom in October, a couple of the guys started to snicker. Mrs. Veinot quieted everyone down and said, "Class, I'd like you all to meet Lester. His family just moved here."

Lester turned out to be really quiet, just sitting in his little desk, watching the goings-on around him and never once putting up his hand or saying anything.

I usually hung with Jake Humber and Cal Seabrooke. They're both okay guys, but like to tease. It shouldn't have surprised me when they decided to track Lester down at recess and give him the official welcome. Cal sidled up to him and says, "Hey, Lester, what's that big pimple growing on your shoulder?"

Then Jake says in his most dramatic voice, "That's not a pimple, Cal, that's his head!"

Lester just shrugs, so Cal says, "I heard a doctor on T.V. say that people with red hair tend to be bed-wetters. Is that true, Lester?"

This time a few more kids joined in the laughing, but Lester just stood there as cool as a cucumber, hands in his pockets, looking at us through those coke bottle glasses of his. Fortunately for him, the bell rang just then, so we all headed back to class.

> Describe how you think Lester must have felt during this time. Why would he feel like that?

Mrs. Veinot had been warning us since the first day of school about a major project on Ancient Civilizations she would be assigning.

We were divided into groups of four, and each group would choose a civilization to research and report on. But wouldn't you know it, when it came to my group, we only had three students — me, Carrie Foster, and good old Lester. What else could possibly go wrong! I was glad to have Carrie in our group — she's a real neat writer and works like a little beaver.

"All right, class," Mrs. Veinot told us, "today your groups will have a chance to work together for one whole period. Half the class will go to the school library with Mrs. Jackson, and the others will remain here."

Our group was picked for the library.

I trudged down to the library and plunked myself at one of the tables. Carrie gave me a funny look.
"What's the matter?" she asked.
"How come she put Lester, the Bed-Wetter with us?" I asked, nodding at Lester, who was just entering the library.

The New Kid

"So what civilization should we do?" She asked, opening her notebook to a fresh page.

Lester just sat there looking down at his mangled fingernails.

"Maybe you'd better explain to Lester what civilization means," I suggested sarcastically.

I was looking over at Lester, giving him my worst scowl when suddenly he grinned! The grin took me completely by surprise because I'd never seen any kind of expression on his face before.

Carrie, being a very serious teacher wanna-be, took me literally and began to give good old Lester a detailed definition of civilization.

Now Lester is looking over at Carrie with this big, stupid grin on his face – only it's not really
stupid at all. Stupid people's eyes don't light up the way Lester's did when he smiled.

> What other expressions can you read in someone's eyes?

When Carrie finally finished her little spiel, Lester turns to me and says, "I might actually be able to help with this project – that is, if you're interested in doing the Aztecs of South America."

Aztecs? I'd never even heard of them before! "I thought we could do the Egyptians," I said. "They'd be real interesting – you know the pyramids and mummies and everything."

"Everyone will be doing the Egyptians," Lester says. "Besides, the Aztecs also built pyramids. My dad works at the museum in the city and they're having a special Aztec display. I think I could arrange a field trip for our class."

Wow! Lester's idea actually sounded pretty good. Mrs. Veinot would probably jump at the chance of taking her class to the museum . . .

"I think the Aztecs are a great idea," Carrie said, turning to me. "What do you think?"

I knew right then that whatever I decided would be really important to Lester. If I backed his idea, and the class got to go to the museum – well, no one would bug him much after that! If, on the other hand, I shot down his idea, Carrie would probably fall into line and things would stay the same for good old Lester .

I looked across the table at Lester, with his messy, red hair, freckles and funny glasses. Never could I remember having to make such a tough decision before—one that might actually change somebody's life . . .

I took a deep breath and tried to look wise and serious—Lester was grinning again, and before I knew it, I was too!

This all happened over a month ago, and since then I've gotten to know Lester a whole lot better, and you know what – he's a really funny guy. Even Cal and Jake think so. Now, if I can just get him to do something about that cowlick on the back of his head!

Name:_____

1. Have you ever met a student that reminds you of Lester? Describe in detail what he/she looked like.

_____

_____

_____

2. Why do you think Cal and Jake teased Lester?

3. Why do you think the boy telling the story (the narrator) didn't try to defend Lester from the teasing?

_____

_____

4. This story features several important decisions. Describe decisions made by the following people:

Mrs. Veinot

The narrator when in the library

5. Was Lester's suggestion regarding the Aztecs a good one? Defend your answer.

_____

_____

6. Choose a word to describe each of these characters:

Lester (　　　　　　　)　　　Carrie (　　　　　　　)

Jake (　　　　　　　)　　　The narrator (　　　　　　　)

Name:_____

1. **D**efine recycling: _____

   _____

   Define conservation: _____

   _____

   Explain why these two topics are so important in today's world.

   _____

   _____

2. **L**ist three things that you or your family use that might be conserved.

   •

   •

   •

3. **I**nvestigate: what is meant by the term urban sprawl? Why is it important to limit this?

   _____

   _____

4. **D**o you think it is important to develop solar and wind power?

   _____

   _____

TRASH

Have you ever taken a good look at the trash that your family throws out each week – or the garbage that leaves your school every day? Much of the garbage that we throw out is just that – garbage – fit only for the landfill site, but a lot of the material that goes into these landfills is being wasted. Think of it. So much of what we use and discard on a daily basis is made from materials. Aluminum pop cans, glass bottles, and steel and plastic products. If we continue to carelessly toss things out, we will soon run out of the material to build cars, buildings, and other important items that we rely on in our everyday lives. If we can't replace something, don't throw it away!

Did you know that in the United States alone, 208 million tons of garbage is generated by people like you and me each year. That's 4.3 pounds per person per day! Of this trash, 1/3 of the total of household trash is packaging. Each year Americans throw away 25 trillion polystyrene cups.

You may think that there is not much that one student can do to help this problem, but you would be surprised to know that even the smallest act can be very important.

Before reading further, give one example of how you might help solve this problem.

Here are four tips we can follow to reduce solid waste, otherwise known as the Four R's: reduce, reuse, recycle, respond.

Reduce. Have you ever bought something from a store (like a package of batteries) and noticed that the package is three times the size of what you are actually buying? If you multiply this package by many thousands that the company produces every month – that's a lot of wasted cardboard or plastic. If we choose to buy products with less packaging we can send a message to companies to reduce this waste.   It is also possible to reduce the amount of disposable items we regularly use – such as polystyrene cups and paper plates. Although it is more inconvenient to wash and dry our china and cutlery, it is a lot more environmentally-friendly.

Reuse. **S**omething you may have never considered before is consciously seeking out reusable products. Often these products are labeled as such (i.e., plastic and glass products). We can also reuse plastic bags, containers and other products. Items that aren't used too often can be borrowed or rented – some of these might even be shared among friends. Finally, instead of throwing out an item no longer used, why not sell it at a garage sale, or donate it to charity?

Recycle. **R**ecycling items are put through a process that makes it possible to create new products out of old materials. When shopping, choose products and containers that can be recycled. You can also make an effort to purchase products made from recycled material. Did you know that the energy saved from recycling one aluminum pop can will run a TV for three hours, and that the energy saved from recycling one glass bottle will operate a 100-watt light bulb for four hours?

Great progress is being made in this area. For instance, every minute an average of 113,204 aluminum beverage cans are recycled. This alone can reduce energy use by 90% and air pollution by 95%. Recycling one ton of paper saves 17 trees, 7,000 gallons of water and 380 gallons of oil – yet the typical office worker throws away 180 pounds of high-grade paper every year.

Composting is another excellent way of recycling. Each year the average person creates about 360 pounds of food and yard waste. Add this to the huge amounts of leaves and grass discarded by the average person and you can see how this can fill up a landfill site very quickly.

What other things can be recycled that aren't mentioned here?

Respond. **W**e can do our part in encouraging our friends and family members to reduce and recycle. We can also find creative ways to reduce waste quantity.

One way that schools can respond is by starting and supporting a school recycling program. A good place to begin is to find out what is in your trash at the school. This is called an audit. Is it mainly paper and cardboard? What other materials are there that can be recycled (e.g., pizza boxes, aluminum cans)? The next thing to do is to find a market for the material, and then work out the details with your market-recycler and custodial staff. This might also be a good fundraiser for your school.

There are many other ways that you can help to keep all of these precious resources from being sent to a landfill site somewhere. You really can make a difference!

Name:_____

TRASH

1. **I**n your own words, describe why the following four points are important:

reduce: _____

reuse: _____

recycle: _____

respond: _____

2. a) **I**nvestigate: why are polystyrene cups such a special problem?

_____

_____

b) **H**ow much solid waste is thrown out by the average American per day?

_____

c) **H**ow can we reduce our need for using so much packaging?

_____

_____

3. a) **D**efine composting: _____

_____

b) **W**hat is your school doing about this important problem?

_____

_____

_____

Name:_____

HERO OF 911

1. What occupations might provide the most opportunities for being heroic?

_____
_____
_____

2. Under what circumstances would you do something heroic?

3. Investigate: In 2 to 3 sentences, tell about a person you consider heroic. What did this person do that was heroic?

_____
_____
_____

4. Investigate: Nelson Mandela is a wonderful example of a hero. Who was he and what did he do that was especially heroic?

_____
_____
_____
_____
_____
_____
_____
_____

5. Name three things for which people would give their lives.

•
•
•

THE MYSTERIOUS RED BANDANA MAN

The events of 9/11 were horrible for everyone. In the chaos, a number of remarkable people became heroes. Firefighters, police officers, medics, and many ordinary citizens risked their lives to lead others to safety from the World Trade Centre in New York City, and some even gave their lives so that others might live.

their son must have been extremely difficult for the Crowthers.

> Why would this have been even harder than finding his body right away?

One such hero was a man who for months was simply known as the "*mysterious man in the red bandana*".

Wells Crowther, 24, worked on the 104th floor of the South Tower and was in his office when the plane struck. At 9:12 that morning, Wells called his mother's cell phone. Although the call did not go through, he left a message saying, "Mom, this is Wells. I want to let you know that I'm okay."

Wells was very athletic, playing both hockey and lacrosse in high school and college. He was also a volunteer firefighter at the Nyack Empire Ladder Company. His comrades remember Wells as a good firefighter who knew his duty.

Despite the phone call and his firefighter training, Wells did not make it out of the South Tower. What happened? For many long months his death remained a mystery. It wasn't until six months later that they finally recovered Wells' body on the ground floor

-The mystery man had appeared on the 78th Floor not long after the plane's impact-

lobby of the South Tower with a group of firefighters. He had gotten all the way to the lobby! What had kept him there when he was only steps away from safety?

Not knowing for sure what happened to

Two months after Wells' body was found, a remarkable story began to emerge about Wells Crowthers' last hours. It began when Wells' dad was reading a story in the local newspaper about 9/11. The story described

THE MYSTERIOUS RED BANDANA MAN

how a woman was saved from certain death in the South Tower.

They were startled to read that "a mysterious man appeared at one point, his mouth and nose covered with a red handkerchief."

Wells' parents knew right then that they were reading about their son, because he always carried a red bandana in his back pocket.

The mystery man had appeared on the 78th Floor not long after the plane's impact. By this time most of the 200 people there were either dead or dying.

The few who survived had no idea what to do in the terrible confusion. At this moment the mystery man with a red bandana covering his nose and mouth pointed to the stairs and said, "Anyone who can walk, get up and walk now. Anyone who can, perhaps help others, find someone who needs help and then head down." In

this way, Wells led many people from certain death to safety.

The people that Wells saved were anxious to know who the mystery man had been who had helped them and what had happened to him.

After Wells' mom and dad saw the article in the newspaper they contacted a couple of the survivors that their son had helped. When these people saw a picture of Wells they immediately said, "That was the man who saved my life. Without him I wouldn't be here."

Wells' parents asked the survivors if there was something in Wells' voice that made them spring into action.

"It was the way he said it," was the answer. "He had such authority that we felt we had to go ahead, do it."

"He was acting as a firefighter in the last hour of his life," his father said.

One of Wells' fellow firefighters said, "He (Wells) would never give up. If he was a soldier in a foxhole, I'd want Wells next to me."

Finally, after many months the mystery of the man in the red bandana was solved.

Why do you think it was important for the survivors to know who it was that saved them?

_____

_____

_____

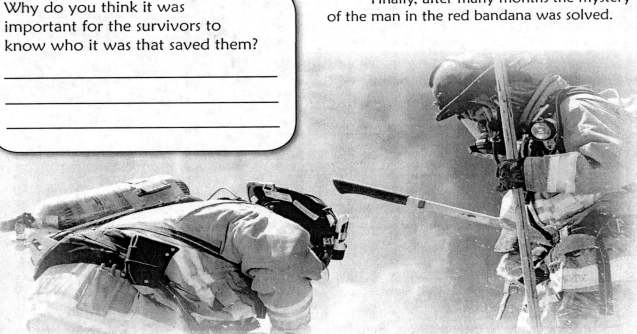

Name:_____

 HERO OF 911

1. Describe what you think it was like for the people in the World Trade Centre when the plane struck. (Be as detailed as possible.)

_____

_____

_____

_____

_____

_____

_____

3. Wells was a very brave man, but he also had something in his background that helped him in this situation. What was it?

4. Why had Wells only gotten as far as the lobby?

2. If you were one of the people that Wells saved, what might you do to show your gratitude?

5. Why did the people respond to Wells when he began telling them what to do?

Monster Trucks

1. Describe what it must feel like to drive a monster truck.

_____

_____

2. If you had the chance to drive a monster truck, where would you take it and what would you do with it?

_____

_____

3. How would it be more difficult to drive a monster truck than a regular pick-up truck?

_____

_____

4. Investigate: What are two things that might happen at a monster truck event?

_____

_____

5. Choose a word from the list to complete each definition:

> **extinguish   incapacitated   fiberglass   restraint   interrupt**

a) The angry teacher showed a lot of _____.

b) A canoe is often made of _____.

c) It is a good idea to _____ a campfire before leaving.

d) It's rude to _____ someone when they're speaking.

e) The driver was _____ because of the crash.

Monster Trucks

Joel Seabrooke, a grade 8 student attending Victoria Parkland
Public School, had the opportunity to interview the
winner of a local monster truck competition
in his hometown. Here is their
fascinating conversation:

Q: What is a monster truck?

A: **The monster truck a highly modified four wheel drive vehicle. What makes it different from other trucks is the extreme oversized tires. Most monster trucks are built to be faster and better-handling than what you might expect, since they are made for racing, running over cars, and ramp-jumping.**

Q: How many monster trucks are there?

A: **Of the 500 monster trucks in the world, there are only 100 or so that are full-blown racing trucks. Others are only for exhibitions, car crushers, or promotional vehicles. The majority of monster trucks are found in the US.**

Q: How big are their tires?

A: **66 inches (165cms) tall by 43 inches (108cms) wide. That's about six inches (15cms) taller than most men. These tires are often used by farmers on fertilizer-spreaders and are called flotation tires because they spread the vehicle's weight across a wider surface. Some monster trucks have even floated on water with these large tires.**

Q: How fast can a monster truck go?

A: **On the quickest courses, drivers can usually get the truck up to 65-70 mph (105-110kmph), although typically indoors, drivers max out at 25-30 mph (40-45kmph).**

Q: How heavy are most monster trucks?

A: **For racing, the bare minimum is 10,000 lbs (4,550 kgs). Older trucks from the early 1980s weighed nearly 20,000 lbs (9,100 kgs). The minimum weight now is 9,500 lbs (4,300 kgs).**

Monster Trucks

Q: How do they move a monster truck from one place to another?

A: They are usually hauled in a heavy duty truck – a semi-trailer.

Q: How do you get into a monster truck?

A: In most of the new fiberglass models, there is a hatch in the floor for the drivers to climb up through. On an older truck, the driver would open the door, grab hold of the seat and door, push off the front tire and haul himself into the truck.

Q: What is a killer box?

A: Officially it is known as the Remote Ignition Interrupter or RII. Quite a mouthful, isn't it? The killer box is a real life-saver, because it is a specialized radio receiver, which has the ability to shut off the engine, should the truck veer off the track and/or the driver lose consciousness.

Q: What does the driver of a monster truck wear?

A: The driver wears a fire resistant suit, gloves, a helmet liner and shoes. Drivers are held into the seat by a standard five way racing harness. Most drivers also wear helmet restraints, and a neck collar. Some drivers may wear a kidney belt to help absorb the impact on the spine and neck. A fire extinguisher must be within the driver's reach!

Q: How much does a monster truck cost?

A: Around $100,000 plus $40,000 for the engine. Don't forget that it is also very expensive to maintain a monster truck throughout the year.

Q: How long does it take to build a monster truck?

A: It can take anywhere from 3 months to a year to build a monster truck. This depends on how much time is put into detail work and how many people are working on the project.

Q: How do I become a monster truck driver?

A: To become a driver, you must be 25 years of age, in good physical shape, and have a current commercial driver's license. A good start is to try to get onto someone's crew. If you make the crew, you would most likely serve two years apprenticeship before learning to drive.

Name:_____

Monster Trucks

1. What is the main thing that makes monster trucks different from other trucks?

2. Measure yourself (in inches). How many inches taller is a monster truck tire than you?

3. Approximately how many racing monster trucks are there in the world?

4. Why are monster trucks equipped with a killer box?

5. List six pieces of equipment worn by a monster truck driver.

_____   _____

_____   _____

_____   _____

6. What's the approximate total cost of a monster truck (including the engine)?

7. The article mentions that it usually takes from three months to a year to build a monster truck. What two factors are mentioned that might influence the time it takes to build one?

Name:_____

Bone Deep

1. A mystery is something like a riddle. See if you can solve this riddle before reading "Bone Deep".

> A father and his son are driving along the highway one stormy night when they are involved in a bad accident. The father is killed and the son is rushed to the local hospital. A surgeon is immediately called to perform an emergency operation on the boy. Upon arrival, the surgeon takes one look at the boy and says, "I can't operate on this boy, he's my son." How is this possible?

2. Have you ever been camping, or read about the dangers of a camping trip? List at least three possible dangers facing campers in the wilderness.

_____ _____ _____

3. One of the characters in "Bone Deep" has a run of bad luck. Put the expression, "It never rains but when it pours", in your own words.

4. Describe a time in your life when nothing seemed to be going right for you (or someone you know).

_____

_____

_____

Bone Deep

Solve this Mystery!

Elephant's Breath is a remote mining town miles from the nearest city. Located in the middle of the wilderness, the area attracts many campers, fishermen and hunters who love canoeing the region's lakes and rivers.

Elephant's Breath has one police officer, whose responsibilities include keeping the peace and solving any crimes which might occur in the region.

One hot summer evening, the police officer is called to the scene of a serious accident. A woman has been struck by a pickup truck on a remote stretch of gravel road not far from town. That particular road runs from Dixon Landing, a popular starting point for canoeists, to the highway—three miles from Elephant's Breath. The canoe route, on the winding Kenogami River, is especially popular among the city dwellers from the south. The injured woman has been taken to the local hospital where she remains in a coma.

The lonely stretch of road where the woman was injured leads to a boat-landing on the river. The police officer realizes that for some unknown reason the woman must have been walking from the river to the highway. Following a hunch, the police officer drives back to the boat-landing and finds the woman's station wagon parked there. The driver's door window is smashed, and the engine hood has been raised. To complicate matters even further, a dead man is found in the back of the car. The man appears to be about 40 years old, and is wearing rough camping clothing. A quick examination of the body reveals that the man died from a severe cut to the inside of his left leg, just above the knee. The police officer has seen such nasty cuts before—only a sharp axe could do such a thing! A search of the man's clothing reveals nothing—not even his personal identification. The police officer also notices a blood-stained canoe pulled up on the shore of the nearby river.

How do you think the canoe got blood-stained? Why might this be an important clue for the police officer?

Bone Deep

Back at the hospital, the police officer searches the woman's belongings, which have been piled on a chair by the door. A red and black plaid checkered shirt catches the police officer's eye. A large brown stain is noticeable down near the bottom, and another brighter stain up by the collar. The stain near the collar looks fresher–perhaps from the bad cut the woman had on her forehead. The stain near the bottom of the jacket, on the other hand, looks older, like it had been from an earlier injury. The police officer picks a small piece of something from the rough material. Glass! Yet there had been no broken glass on the truck that struck her.

Other than clothing, the only items recovered are: a wallet containing her driver's licence, one credit card and $230; a blood-stained handkerchief; a package of matches; and a compass. Her name is Marjorie Beckworth, and she is from the city, although the scant belongings tell the police officer little else. There's no packsack or camping gear . . . even back at the car there had been no tent . . . no axe!

What happened here? The police officer wonders. A man is dead and a woman is in a coma–and no witnesses can be called upon to help unravel the mystery. Was it an accident–or was it something far worse–like murder?

It is obvious that the two people had been out on a camping trip, leaving the car here at the landing while they canoed the peaceful waters of the area. But how did the man receive his injuries? And how did he end up in the back of the station wagon? Most importantly, what was the woman doing out on the road in the middle of the night? Why didn't she just drive the car to the local hospital and get help for the injured man?

> What do you think happened that resulted in the woman being out on the lonely road to town, where she was run over? The police officer from Elephant's Breath is stumped, so it is entirely up to you to solve the mystery. Consider: Why did she leave her husband in the car and walk to town (Why didn't she just drive)? How did the man receive the cut on his leg? Good luck!

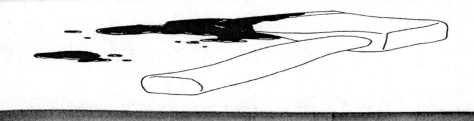

Name:_____

Bone Deep

1. Do you think the police officer is a man or a woman? Try to support your answer with proof from the story.

_____

_____

2. Why might it be more difficult for this police officer to solve such a mystery than the police force of a large city?

_____

_____

3. The setting of "Bone Deep" is rather unique. Compare the setting to the one in which you live, using three points of comparison in the following chart:

Points of Comparison (i.e., size)	Elephant's Breath	Where You Live
•	•	•
•	•	•
•	•	•

4. What do you think happened to cause the man to die and the woman to be injured?

Name:_____

That's One Hanukkah of a Party

1. Describe what takes place on the following holidays or tell what they celebrate. You may have to do some research.

   Christmas

   The Fast of Ramadan

   The Passover

   Chinese New Year

2. What is your favorite holiday not including the summer holidays? Why?

3. Why are holidays important to society?

4. Why is it valuable to respect the traditions and celebrations of other cultures and religions?

   _____

   _____

   _____

   _____

5. Why do you think the celebrations of other cultures that are different from your own sometimes seem strange? How might we change this?

   _____

   _____

   _____

That's One Hanukkah of a Party

Last week, my mom decided at the last minute to go with my dad on one of his business trips to the city for the weekend. Usually I would stay with my Aunt Sheila, but this time I asked if I could spend the weekend at my friend Daniel's place.

So my mom called his mom and it was settled. The only possible glitch in our plans was the fact that Daniel's family were in the middle of celebrating something called Hanukkah.

"Don't worry," Daniel said when I suggested that maybe we should just forget about it and I should stay with my aunt, "Hanukkah's fun – kind of like your Christmas."

"My Christmas" I said. "Doesn't your family have Christmas?"

"We're Jewish – so some of our holidays are different. During Hanukkah, for instance, we give presents to one another just like you do at Christmas. We won't be doing that tonight though because we exchanged presents the other day."

I just nodded. It was difficult to imagine someone not having Christmas.

Do you or any of your friends celebrate any days or events? If so, what are they?

"So what's Hanukkah all about anyway?" I asked on our way to his place.

"Well, my mom calls it the Festival of Lights. That's because candles are a big part of the holiday. And unlike your Christmas, which only lasts for a day, Hanukkah lasts for eight days. This year it begins on November 30th and ends on December 7th."

"What do you actually celebrate on Hanukkah?" I asked. "I mean on Christmas we celebrate the birth of Jesus Christ."

We celebrate a great victory that our people won many, many years ago against an army that was invading Israel. The victory was considered a miracle and Jewish legend says that after the victory, when the Temple was being rededicated, only one jar of oil was found, which was enough light for only one day. Miraculously, the oil burned for eight days. That's why we have the eight days of Hanukkah.

Daniel was right about candles being important, for there in the middle of the dinner table was a large candleholder they called a menorah. It held eight candles, seven of which were burning.

The meal began with Daniel's dad saying a short prayer, then we dug into one of the tastiest meals I've ever had. There was chicken, corn and a special kind of pancake that they

That's One Hanukkah of a Party

called latkes which we dipped in apple sauce. They tasted really crispy on the outside, but soft inside.

For dessert we had something called sufganiyot, which was a jelly doughnut without the hole. The sufganiyots were passed around in a big basket and although they looked kind of funny, because each one was a different shape, they sure tasted good. I could have eaten a dozen.

Daniel said that eating latkes and sufganiyots were traditional during Hanukkah - kind of like eating turkey at Christmas and pumpkin pie at Thanksgiving.

After dinner Daniel's dad brought out this strange-looking gadget that looked like a spinning top. Daniel said it was called a dreidel. His dad then gave everybody a dozen large chocolate mints. He then had each of us put one of our mints in the kitty. We then took turns spinning the dreidel. The dreidel would fall on one of four letters, the Num meant that no one won the kitty, the Gimmel meant you would take everything from the kitty, the Heh meant you would take half, and the Peh meant you lost what you put in. It was a riot. Daniel's mom won the most mints, but I still ended up with eight when the game was over.

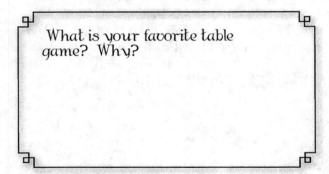

What is your favorite table game? Why?

Just before Daniel and I headed up to his room, his dad said that they had one last ceremony to share. Daniel's mom brought back the menorah and set it in the middle of the table.

"You may have noticed that there is still one candle unlit," Daniel's dad said.

I nodded.

"Well, today is the eighth day of Hanukkah, so we will be lighting the last candle. With that he took the middle candle and held it for a second over the unlit candle at the far end. As the candle flickered to life, Daniel's dad said in a kind of sing-song voice, "Blessed are you, Lord our God, King of the universe, who performed miracles for our fathers in days of old at this season."

Daniel and his parents then sang a really nice song, which kind of reminded me of one of the hymns we sing at church.

So all in all it was a really interesting experience, and it was great to get to know what people of other faiths believe. I told Daniel he could come over to my place on Christmas day if he wants to. In the meantime I've noticed that another guy in my class doesn't celebrate some of the same holidays as the rest of us either. He told me he was born in India and is Hindu. I think it would be interesting to get to know more of what he and his family celebrate. There sure is a lot I don't know about the way that different people do things, right here in my own classroom!

Name:_____

That's One Hanukkah of a Party

1. Daniel compares Hanukkah with Christmas. List two similarities and two differences between these two special days.

Similarities	Differences
•	•
•	•

2. What is a menorah?

_____

_____

_____

3. What is a dreidel and for what is it used?

_____

_____

_____

4. What value is there in getting to know more about someone else's culture?

_____

_____

_____

5. Investigate. The narrator mentions a boy in the class from India who is a Hindu. What are some traditional foods of many people from India?

_____

_____

_____

_____

 THE HIRED HAND

1. From what you know about owning a pet, what advantages are there for someone your age owning and caring for a cat or dog?

2. What might the disadvantages be?

3. Investigate the general characteristics of the terrier breed of dog (Find out three things).

   •   •   •

4. What is your favorite breed of dog? Why?

5. Replace the words that are underlined in the sentences below with a word from the word list in the box. Remember to consider the context of the word, as some words have several meanings.

| vermin | characteristic | placid | intent | absolute | tolerance |

The loud laugh was <u>typical</u> of my friend.   _____

The sea was very <u>calm</u> this morning.   _____

He has a real <u>understanding</u> of dogs.   _____

He was <u>wrapped up</u> in his book.   _____

The farmer considers the weasel to be a harmful <u>varmint</u>. _____

The flood left the house in an <u>extreme</u> mess.   _____

THE HIRED HAND

B rady didn't mind living with his grandparents except for one thing – Grandpa wouldn't let him have a dog. He'd coaxed and pleaded until his grandma said, "Listen, Brady, you'd better drop the matter because your grandfather's mind is made up."

"But why does he hate dogs so much? He's a farmer."

"Brady, it's important to your grandfather that all of our farm animals have a purpose. Your grandfather thinks pets are just a waste of his hard-earned money."

How do you think Brady will be able to change his grandfather's mind?

One hot summer afternoon a week or two later, just when Brady was beginning to think that getting a dog was an absolute pipe dream, someone dropped a dog off at the end of their laneway – then roared away in a cloud of dust.

Brady couldn't believe it. The medium-sized dog was tan-colored, with bowed legs, a long, square head, and a tuft of whiskers hanging from its chin.

A terrier! For months he'd been reading about different breeds and studying their pictures. He knew that terriers tended to be hyper and yappy, yet this particular one just sat there in the middle of the driveway looking up at him with the most curious expression.

As Brady approached the dog it cocked its head to one side, eyeing him curiously. Brady checked for a collar. There was none.

"What am I going to do with you?" he asked sadly. "Grandpa will never let me keep you, yet you seem like such a nice dog." He hesitated.

"Well, we might as well go and face the music." Brady turned and started up the laneway, and the dog immediately trotted along behind him.

"You sure are good-natured," Brady admitted. "Not as yappy and hyper as the books say you are."

At the farmhouse Brady left the dog in the yard and found his grandmother at the kitchen counter making bread.

"Grandma, somebody dropped a dog off at the end of the laneway."

His grandmother nodded. "I saw you bring it up here. What kind is it?"

"A terrier mix, by the look of it."

Grandma kept kneading the dough. "What do you know about terriers?"

Brady hesitated. "They're inclined to be a bit yappy," he admitted.

"Not exactly a favorite characteristic of most dog-owners."

THE HIRED HAND

"I know," Brady said. "Grandpa doesn't even like good, quiet dogs."

The older woman looked up from her work. "That's not the point, Brady. I doubt if it'd make any difference to your grandfather how good-natured a dog is. He's only interested in having them earn their keep."

"Too bad we don't have any sheep. I could train it to be a sheepdog."

"Dogs were bred to be the way they are for particular reasons. Why don't you do a little research and see what you can come up with?"

Brady frowned thoughtfully. What was his grandmother trying to tell him? With a puzzled frown he ran up to his room, retrieved several of his dog books, then returned to the yard. The dog was waiting patiently by the rose bush.

Brady dropped to the ground and opened the first book to the section on terriers. Cairn terriers, Jack Russells, Scotties . . . With each breed Brady would turn to the dog beside him and compare him to the accompanying photograph.

"I think you look most like the Irish Terrier," he finally said.

The dog wagged its tail.

"Now what does it say about the Irish Terrier?" Wiry coats . . . little tolerance of other animals.

He looked again at the dog. "You seem to be a very tolerant fellow."

Bred to hunt and kill vermin. Brady's ears perked up. Irish terriers are especially good at bringing to ground: rats, mice, and even foxes and weasels.

That was it! Now he knew what his grandmother had been trying to tell him. Their henhouse was so old it was becoming difficult to keep predators out – and there was no money to build a new one. Just the other day, his grandfather had complained about a weasel killing a couple of his chickens, and this past spring, a fox had killed over a dozen hens in less than fifteen minutes . . .

He scrambled to his feet and raced to the kitchen.

"Grandma, I've got it! The dog can earn its keep by guarding the henhouse against weasels and foxes. Terriers were bred to kill vermin."

"So they were," his grandmother said with a faint smile. "When I was a little girl my father kept a terrier for that very purpose. I was hoping you'd find out for yourself - and with a little research, you did."

"Thanks, Grandma," Brady said with a big grin. "Now we just have to convince Grandpa to keep him."

"Oh, I think that will be up to the dog. If he turns out to be a good guard dog, he'll be worth his weight in gold. If not . . ." She paused and smiled. "If our little friend has found a home here, what are you going to call him?"

Brady thought for a minute. "I'm going to call him Handy - short for The Hired Hand," he said. "Just to remind Grandpa that this is one dog who will be out there everyday, protecting our chickens and earning his keep."

> Earlier in the story Grandma refers to the dog as it. At the end of the story, she refers to the dog as him. Why do you think she made this change?

THE HIRED HAND

1. Why wouldn't Brady's grandfather let him have a dog?

_____

_____

2. Give one example of how Brady's grandmother proved she was a wise woman.

_____

_____

_____

3. What did Brady know about the terrier breed *before* doing further research?

_____

_____

_____

4. What further information about the breed did Brady discover through his research?

_____

_____

_____

5. How did Brady think he might be able to convince his grandfather to let him keep the dog?

_____

_____

_____

Name:_____

 # DEALING WITH FAILURE

1. Why do you think it is so difficult for a person to handle failure?

2. How might experiencing failure help one deal with similar experiences later in life?

3. In order to be a success in life, what is one important character trait for a person to have?

4. Who is the most successful person you know personally?

5. Why do you consider this person to be a success?

6. Why do you think this person has been such a success?

DEALING WITH FAILURE

Sometimes life seems very hard and unfair, doesn't it? It is easy to get discouraged when you look around you and see how easy other people have it – how their families have more money for things, or maybe they are better-looking, and seem smarter and more athletic. You may even wonder if someone like yourself could ever be successful in life. You can!

List three good things about yourself.

-
-
-

Years ago a young boy was born into a very poor family. The boy's parents eked out a living as poor farmers for many years, but in order to survive he had to help his family by working long, hard hours with the farm chores. When he was only seven years old he and his family left their home and all of his friends and moved far away to where his father had bought a new farm.

Only two years after their move, tragedy visited the small household. The boy's mother got very sick and died – an event that left a great mark on him for the rest of his life. He was only nine years old.

Like many children of his time, the boy did not have the opportunity to attend school regularly, but he was determined to learn to read and write – and he did – spending long hours practicing and improving his skills.

He left home at a young age and got a job as a store clerk, but lost his position a year later when the business failed. Later, he was appointed postmaster of his township and ended up having the worst efficiency record in the county. Not a very good start in the work force, was it?

In one sentence, describe the man's life and accomplishments so far.

As a young man he fell in love with a woman named Ann Rutledge. Her sudden death sent him into a terrible depression. It is even possible that he had a nervous breakdown at this time.

DEALING WITH FAILURE

It was during this unsettling time of his life that he developed an interest in politics and decided to run for the state legislature. You can imagine his disappointment when he lost – placing eighth among 13 candidates.

Although all of these early setbacks must have been terribly discouraging, they were not enough to keep this determined young man from pursuing his dreams.

Eventually he did succeed in winning a seat in the state legislature and continued to gain the respect and admiration of everyone who knew him.

Even as he became more successful as a lawyer and politician, he experienced great tragedy. His son died at the age of four, and he failed to be elected to both the senate and the vice presidency.

Finally in 1860 he ran for the presidency of the United States. Not only did he win the election, he went on to become one of the greatest leaders in his country's history. The man's name was Abraham Lincoln.

> From what you have read about Abraham Lincoln in this article, choose one word you feel best describes him.

Imagine if Abraham Lincoln had let his early failures and discouragements defeat him. Imagine if this great man had just given up and decided that he wasn't good enough – or that he didn't have anything to offer. Americans then wouldn't have had this wise and gracious man's leadership through the darkest years of their history – the great Civil War.

Abraham is an inspiring example of someone who faced great tragedy, failure and disappointment and continued to persevere until he realized his greatest dream, and made a difference to the world around him.

Looking back at the great trials that Lincoln went through as a boy and as a young man, we can now see how this prepared him for even greater hardships he would face as president.

In the middle of the terrible Civil War, Lincoln did a remarkable thing. He issued the following proclamation to the American people: "It has seemed to me fit and proper that (the gifts of God) should be solemnly, reverently, and gratefully acknowledged with one heart and one voice by the whole American people. I do, therefore, invite my fellow citizens . . . to set apart and observe the last Thursday of November next as a day of thanksgiving and praise to our benevolent Father who dwelleth in the heavens."

Abraham Lincoln was a remarkable man, who despite a life filled with trials, as well as tremendous accomplishments, found that there is much to be thankful for.

Name:_____

DEALING WITH FAILURE

1. List six things in Lincoln's life that you would consider as either hardships, tragedies or failures.

  -
  -
  -
  -
  -
  -

2. Describe what Lincoln's childhood was like.

3. What would you consider Lincoln's greatest hardship, tragedy or failure?

4. Why is Lincoln considered by many people to be a great man?

5. What holiday did Lincoln begin during the Civil War?

6. Why did some people probably think this was an odd holiday to begin during the middle of a war?

Name:_____

SKATEBOARD PARK

1. Skateboarding is a very demanding sport. What physical attributes do you think are important in order to be a good skateboarder?

   _____

   _____

2. Name 2 to 3 similarities and 2 to 3 differences between skateboarding and snowboarding.

   Similarities   Differences

   -
   -

   -
   -

3. What are a couple of important features of a skateboard park?

   _____

4. Investigate: Tony Hawk is the world's most famous skateboarder. Find out three interesting facts about him.

5. Draw a line to match the correct definition of each word. Use a dictionary to help you, if necessary.

   a) manoeuver   newcomer

   b) feature   movement

   c) tremendous   depend

   d) spectator   appearance

   e) rely   great

   f) novice   fan

SKATEBOARD PARK

Skateboard parks are springing up all over North America. These parks are a welcome addition to many neighborhoods, giving skateboarders a place of their own to gather and practice their many manoeuvers.

Parks commonly boast such features as smooth skating surfaces, and modern equipment including ramps, quarter and half pipes, bank ramps, spines and grind rails. Some even include a bleacher section for spectators.

To ensure the total enjoyment of all skaters, some parks are divided into beginner, intermediate and advanced sections.

Why would having three such sections add to the enjoyment of all skaters?

If you don't have a skateboard park in your neighborhood you might be able to start building your own, which isn't as difficult as you might think. All you need is time and the willingness to round up a little cash.

First you need to decide what you are going to build. A simple ramp or rail can be built in a couple of hours, while a halfpipe might take you and your peeps a couple of weeks. Having a well thought-out plan can save you a lot of hassles. In this regard, getting the help of your parents or other adults can be useful.

Some ideas to get you going might include talking to a shop teacher at your local high school to see if they might build a ramp or half pipe as a class project, using tools and supplies from the school for the project. Another possibility is asking your parents for building supplies instead of clothes for your birthday. You and your friends might also pool your money together. Don't forget that plans for building rails, halfpipes and other ramps can be downloaded free from different Internet sites. It is important that both the design and the construction of the park be solid.

SKATEBOARD PARK

The construction of all parks must be safe for users. Make sure that the finished product is checked over by a qualified adult before the first skater tries it out. Skateboarding is difficult enough without having to contend with a rail or ramp collapsing during a performance.

> Can you think of any other ideas for helping you design and build your own park?

It is also important when building a park to rely on the experts as much as possible when it comes to design, so such things as height restrictions don't ruin your finished facility. When skills outgrow such a park, it can be filled with boredom and frustration. A good skateboard park should be fluid, diverse and challenging. With a single push, one should be able to skate the entire park.

The height should be from eight to twelve feet. Other key features might include the dragon rail, the volcano, and a kidney pool. Many parks are now made of concrete – a tremendous upgrade from homemade wooden ramps and an asphalt slab.

A typical skateboard park will include quarter pipes with:

- 12-foot walls
- bank ramps with a ledge
- street spine (3'h x 8'w)
- launch land (4'h x 8'w x 24'l)
- half pipes (4'h x 126'w x 28'l)
- grind rails (24" x 8" x 18')
- novice equipment including a bank ramp (3'h x 7'w)
- quarter pipe (2'h x 6'w) and double bank (2'h x 6'w)

Skateboarding is a great way to develop coordination, balance and stamina. An accomplished skateboarder requires hours and hours of practice to become very good. But once a number of different manoeuvers have been mastered, it provides the boarder with a great sense of self-satisfaction. What a wonderful thing it is for the thousands of skateboarders around the world to have so many top-notch parks in which to perfect their craft.

SKATEBOARD PARK

1. Why is it a good thing for a skater to be able to skate an entire park with a single push?

   _____

   _____

2. What are four different components of a skateboard park?

   •   •

   •   •

3. The article mentions several suggestions for raising money/help to build your own park. Brainstorm ideas with two or three other students to come up with a couple of additional ideas.

4. This article makes a number of suggestions as to what items might be included in a park. What are three items you would be sure to include?

   •   •   •

5. How does skateboarding provide the participant with a real sense of self-satisfaction?

Name:_____

GIRLS ARE TALLER

1. Do a quick survey of the students in your class. How many girls are there? How many of the girls are taller than you? Look at your results. Do they back up the title of this story?

2. If it is true that many girls are taller than boys, why do you think girls are taller than boys the same age? If this statement is true, do you think it bothers some boys? Why?

3. Even if it's true that many girls are taller than boys of the same age, what advantage do many boys have over girls of the same age?

4. In each of the following sets of words, underline the one word which does not belong.

a) conscious	aware	ignorant	atuned
b) patient	calm	edgy	tolerant
c) suggest	hint	imply	demand
d) puberty	adolescence	teenage	infancy

GIRLS ARE TALLER

It's not enough that a lot of girls are smarter than boys in the seventh grade, some are even taller too! Bradley, Munroe and I were talking about this very thing at school the other day, when who should come walking by but Mr. Glieberman, who was our teacher in grade six.

"How's it going, guys?" he says with that big grin of his.

Everybody likes Mr. G. In fact he's still my favorite teacher, although I probably wouldn't want him to know that.

"Not much," I said.

But old Bradley pipes in, "We were just talking about how a lot of the girls in our class are taller than us, Mr. G."

Munroe and I groaned. Who wants to talk about something like that with a teacher - even Mr. G.

"You guys got a minute?" he asks.

We all kind of looked at each other and didn't say anything.

"Then come on into my classroom for a minute and I'll tell you what I know."

> If you were going to talk to an adult about a topic like this, who would it be?

So Mr. G. leads us down the hallway to his classroom, with Munroe and I giving Bradley dirty looks behind Mr. G.'s back.

Once in the room Mr. G. plops down at a big table at the back of the room and we pull up chairs and sit down around him.

"When I was your age it used to really bug me that so many girls were taller than me," he says.

I was kind of surprised at that. It was kind of hard to picture Mr. G. being in grade 7, even though he's a lot younger than my dad.

Mr. G.'s got this little grin on his face. "The main reason why some girls are taller than you guys is the fact that they get a head start on puberty. Do you remember what puberty means?"

I could feel my neck getting red just hearing the word, puberty.

"Sure," Bradley says. "That's when we have a growth spurt. Our voices change, we get body hair and we sweat a lot."

Monroe and I laugh awkwardly.

"That's right," Mr. G. says. "Girls tend to start puberty somewhere between the ages of 8 and 13, whereas boys tend to start a couple of years later. It's also a time when people tend to really feel self-conscious about what's going on with their bodies. During puberty most kids feel that they are too fat, too skinny, too tall, too short. It's difficult not to compare what is happening with your own body to what's going on with your friends." We all go through puberty differently, but sooner or later, everyone catches up."

Bradley laughed. "I remember you telling us about all that stuff in Health class, Mr. G."

GIRLS ARE TALLER

"Don't forget that genetics are important in deciding how tall you become too," he said.

"What's that?" Monroe asked.

"Well, if your mom and dad are tall, there's a real good chance that you're going to be tall too, eventually that is."

"My mom's real short," Bradley said. "She has to sit on a cushion when she drives."

"If you're really concerned about not growing fast enough you can always talk to your doctor," Mr. G. suggested. "He can give you a check-up and tell if everything's okay. Don't forget, there's even a lot of movie stars who are short - like Tom Cruise."

> Can you think of another famous person who is/was short?

"Is there any way to get taller?" Bradley asked.

Mr. G. drew in a deep breath. "Time, Brad, my man. That's the only thing that will make you taller. Not pills, not exercise, not lifting weights. You just have to be patient and wait for nature to kick in."

"That's easier said than done, Mr. G," I said.

"I know it is, but try not to let what you see on television and the movies put pressure on you. They're always trying to tell you what you should look like and how you should feel about yourself.

"But I'll bet you never had to worry about girls being taller than you," Munroe says. "You must be almost six feet tall."

Mr. G. laughed, then got to his feet. "Come on up to my desk, fellas, I want to show you something."

He led us up to his big messy desk, then rummaged around in the long drawer for a minute before fishing out a beat up old class picture. Mr. G. pointed to a curly-haired boy at the end of the first row.

"Is that you?" Monroe asked.

Mr. G. nodded. "Why you must be the shortest kid in the class," Bradley finally said.

"Well, not quite," Mr. G. replied, "But I was one of the shorter ones alright. It wasn't until the summer before grade ten that I finally sprouted up."

"Way to go, Mr. G." I said, smiling up at him. "Maybe there's hope for us yet."

Mr. G. laughed. "No doubt about it," he said with a Scottish accent, then he turned back to the picture. "But one thing that still bugs me." He pointed to a pretty, tall blond haired girl in the back row. "See that girl there," he said. We all crowded closer. "That's Selena Watkins. She was in my class all through high school, and she was always taller than me - she probably still is."

Name:_____

GIRLS ARE TALLER

1. Why would the boys feel awkward about speaking to an adult about puberty?

2. What is your impression of Bradley? Describe his personality.

3. Why do most kids feel self-conscious about their bodies during puberty?

4. How did Mr. G. prove to the boys that he was unsatisfied with his height in grade 7?

5. What is the only thing that will make a person taller?

6. If you were one of these boys, would you have found Mr. G.'s talk helpful? Explain your answer.

Answer Key

Backyard Sleepover: *(page 8)*
Before Reading:
1. Answers may vary.
2. Answers may vary. (e.g., flashlight, sleeping bag, snacks)
3. Answers may vary. (e.g., at the lake, in a treehouse)
4. stash: a supply of something; platform: a stage; whimper: a soft cry; excitable: easily aroused

During Reading: Probably scared

After Reading:
1. Answers may vary.
2. He was away on a camping trip.
3. Answers may vary.
4. excitable, talkative
5. He was probably a lot of fun.
6. Answers may vary. (e.g., higher walls, better roof, a door, windows)
7. They could have gone down the ladder and had a closer look.

The Sidehill Gouger: *(page 11)*
Before Reading:
1. Answers may vary.
2. Answers may vary.
3. Larger than life characters; exaggerated storyline; admirable characters
4. peculiar – odd; nocturnal – active at night; gouge – to dig; abode – home; emphatic – forceful

During Reading: Answers may vary.

After Reading:
1. Sides of hills
2. They developed two longer legs on the one side of their bodies from years of digging their homes into the sides of hills.
3. chock-full – filled; critters – animals; varmints – pesty animals; peculiar abode – unusual home
4. Answers may vary.
5. Answers may vary.

Platypus Meets the Big Bad Wolf: *(page 14)*
Before Reading:
1. Answers may vary. (e.g., lays eggs; broad, flat tail; webbed feet; snout resembles a duck's bill; lives on land and water)
2. *Three Little Pigs*; wolves are usually portrayed as scary and vicious.
3. ogres, giants, trolls, bears 4. speed, ability to climb trees, fly, swim or crawl into a deep hole

During Reading: Answers may vary.

After Reading:
1. He pretends to be a mutant which was caused by nuclear waste.
2. Answers may vary.
3. Answers may vary.
4. An organism that has undergone a change resulting in the creation of a new character or trait.
5. Cecil decides he had better not risk eating the platypus because he might get sick.

Will Smith: *(page 17)*
Before Reading:
1. Answers may vary. (e.g., acting/singing talent; charisma; confidence)
2. Will is very personable and is also a good actor and rapper.
3. Answers may vary.
4. Charisma: personal quality which arouses popular devotion and enthusiasm. Answers may vary.
5. **a)** do   **b)** try out   **c)** put forward   **d)** character   **e)** let down   **f)** grow

During Reading: Answers may vary; he spent six years acting in a sitcom.

After Reading:
1. Answers may vary.
2. *Enemy of the State*; *Bad Boys II*; *Men in Black*; *Men in Black II*; *Legend of Bagger Vance*; *Wild, Wild West*; *Six Degrees of Separation*; *Made in America*; *Where the Day Takes You*
3. Answers may vary.
4. Answers may vary.
5. Answers may vary.

Making the Team: *(page 20)*
Before Reading:
1. Answers may vary.
2. Answers may vary. (e.g., pride; feeling of success)
3. Answers may vary. (e.g., sad; feeling that he isn't as good as others)
4. Answers may vary. (e.g., good attitude; coachability; gets along with others)
5. Answers may vary.

During Reading: Answers may vary.

After Reading:
1. This helps a player improve his skills.

2. Answers may vary. (e.g., not retaliating and taking a penalty when fouled)
3. Answers may vary. 4. He listens to his coach and works on putting his suggestions to work.
5. Answers may vary. 6. Ask the coach where you need to improve and work on this area.

Local Boy Sets World Record: *(page 23)*
Before Reading:
1. Answers may vary. 2. Answers may vary.
3. Having an authority there to document it. 4. Answers may vary. (e.g., dragonfly)

During Reading: Answers may vary.

After Reading:
1. They wanted to do something different. 2. To jump 20 outhouses on a BMX bike.
3. He crashed into the last outhouse. 4. Answers may vary.
5. Answers may vary. (e.g., Donnie received national recognition.)

Big Sister: *(page 26)*
Before Reading:
1. Answers may vary. 2. Answers may vary.
3. Answers may vary. (e.g., scary, nervous, exciting. It's something new and unfamiliar.)
4. Answers may vary.

During Reading: Answers may vary.

After Reading:
1. He had to go to the washroom suddenly and when he came out, he couldn't find his class.
2. Answers may vary. (e.g., He could have asked the teacher to wait for him.)
3. Answers may vary. (e.g., scared, nervous, embarrassed) 4. Answers may vary.
5. His sister came through for him during a difficult time when she could have just ignored or teased him.
6. Answers may vary. (e.g., she rolls her eyes when he's in trouble; she isn't afraid to look into the shop classroom and then tells him to go in)

Captured by Aliens: *(page 29)*
Before Reading:
1. Answers may vary.
2. Answers may vary. (e.g., telling a lie might create the habit of lying. Lying often gets you into bigger trouble. Others may no longer believe you.)
3. Answers may vary. 4. Easily fooled. Answers may vary.

During Reading: Answers may vary (e.g., to get out of trouble; overactive imagination)

After Reading:
1. Answers may vary. 2. What kind of weapons the Earth has, how big the Earth's armies are.
3. He broke the car window and put a big hole in the wall. 4. Answers may vary.

The Dingledorf: *(page 32)*
Before Reading:
1. Answers may vary. 2. Answers may vary.
3. Answers may vary. 4. A large extinct mammal resembling the elephant.

During Reading: Answers may vary.

After Reading:
1. Answers may vary. 2. dingledorf – not very clever; toad – clumsy; camel – rude
3. c 4. four toes on front feet, five on hind feet
5. The poet fell and squashed him. 6. when they are annoyed or feel threatened

Tear it Up: *(page 35)*
Before Reading:
1. Answers may vary.
2. Answers may vary. (e.g., getting to remote places, hunting, fishing, camping, racing)
3. Answers may vary. (e.g., wear a helmet; don't speed; don't go fast around sharp corners)
4. Answers may vary. (e.g., the product name, price, why it needs to be purchased, a picture or description)

After Reading:
1. 6 hp engine; automatic transmission; studded tires; steel fenders; heavy duty roller chain; big steel chain guard; hand brake; adjustable handlebar clamps; inexpensive; designed for off-road use; engine is smooth and quiet; low center of gravity; uses regular gas 2. His fans might be influenced.
3. It is only his opinion. 4. eight

Jackie Chan: *(page 38)*
Before Reading:
1. Answers may vary. 2. Answers may vary.

3. Answers may vary.   4. Answers may vary.
5. an actor who performs difficult feats that reqire skill and daring

During Reading: to make it appear real

After Reading:
1. many injuries including three broken noses, ankle, fingers, cheekbones and skull
2. Answers may vary. (To look more western.)
3. humor   4. Answers may vary. (e.g., appeal to a wider audience, not just kung fu fans)
5. slapstick comedy

The Unknown Dwarf Planet: *(page 41)*
Before Reading:
1. Sun   2. Nine   3. Mars   4. Venus   5. Mercury   6. dwarf planet   7. One   8. F   9. T
10. *astronomer* – studies outer space
    orbit – revolve
    debris – rubble
    researcher – investigator
    telescope – instrument that magnifies distant objects

    debate – argue
    variety – assortment
    dwarf planet – small, irregular distant planet
    recently – immediately before the present

During Reading: It's so far away and was discovered so recently.

After Reading:
1. Answers may vary.
2. They are too small; don't have the same orbit as other planets; made up of icy debris.
3. **a)** One-fifth the size of our moon.   **b)** 1930   **c)** Bigger than Pluto.
4. Jupiter – Mercury – Earth – Venus – Uranus – Earth

Treasure Map: *(page 44)*
Before Reading:
1. Answers may vary. (e.g., buried treasures, sword fights, parrots, pirate flags, ships, deserted islands)
2. Answers may vary. (e.g., to hide until a safer time)
3. Answers may vary. (e.g., gold coins, jewelry, money)
4. Answers may vary.
5. The Bermuda Triangle is a region in the Pacific Ocean where many ships and planes have disappeared.
6. Answers may vary.

During Reading: Answers may vary.

After Reading:
1. Answers may vary.   2. Answers may vary.
3. Answers may vary.
4. He lost most of his crew to mutiny and sickness and felt they could not defend the treasure at that time.
5. He felt he was dying.

A Risky Ride: *(page 48)*
Before Reading:
1. a-5; b-3; c-7; d-6; e-2; f-1; g-4
2. Answers may vary. (e.g., cold, open water, falling off, hitting a tree)
3. Answers may vary. (e.g., heavy coat, hat with ear flaps, extra pants, warm boots, mitts; survival items: matches in ziplock bag, compass, flares, cell phone)
4. Answers may vary.

During Reading: Answers may vary; Answers may vary; He would get stuck for sure.

After Reading:
1. He was snowmobiling in the wilderness, crossed a slush-covered river and couldn't return the way he came. How would he get back home?   2. Answers may vary. (e.g., walk home)
3. The snowmobile will get stuck and freeze into the water.
4. The faster he went, the better his chances of staying on top of the slush.
5. So they can look for him if he doesn't return on time.

The New Kid: *(page 52)*
Before Reading:
1. Answers may vary. (e.g., nervous)   2. When someone's feelings are hurt.
3. They may look or act differently than others.   4. Answers may vary.
5. We are afraid of being rejected. Perhaps others will start to tease us.

During Reading: Answers may vary.; Fear, love, joy, anger, etc.

After Reading:
1. Answers may vary.
2. They were bullies and gained attention from others in this way.
3. probably afraid of rejection
4. *Mrs. Veinot* – She put Lester in the narrator's group. *Narrator* – Accepted Lester's idea.
5. Answers may vary. (e.g., It was unusual and involved a field trip.)
6. Answers may vary. *Lester* – nerdy, quiet, funny; *Carrie* – serious; *Jake* – bully. *Narrator* – nice, a follower

Trash!: *(page 56)*

Before Reading:
1. To get useful materials from waste to use again; to save; we are running out of many substances that are important.
2. Answers may vary.
3. The spread of cities; cities are using up valuable farmland.
4. They are renewable; we won't run out of them.

During Reading: Answers may vary.

After Reading:
1. Answers may vary.
   b) 4.3 pounds.
3. a) To convert vegetable matter into fertilizer
2. a) They are not biodegradable.
   c) Don't have packages that are so large
   b) Answers may vary.

Hero of 911 – The Mysterious Red Bandana Man: *(page 60)*

Before Reading:
1. Answers may vary.
2. Answers may vary. (e.g., police officer, firefighter, armed services, medical profession)
3. Answers may vary.
4. He fought to end Apartheoid in South Africa even though he was sent to jail. He forgave people for wrongdoing.
5. Answers may vary.

During Reading: Answers may vary; Answers may vary.

After Reading:
1. Answers may vary.
2. Answers may vary.
3. He was a volunteer firefighter.
4. He was intent on helping others escape.
5. Because of his authoritative voice and manner.

Monster Trucks: *(page 64)*

Before Reading:
1. Answers may vary.
2. Answers may vary.
3. Answers may vary.
4. car-crushings, rodeo, races
5. a) restraint; b) fiberglass; c) extinguish; d) interrupt; e) incapacitated

After Reading:
1. The large tires
2. Answers may vary.
3. 500
4. In case the driver is incapacitated or the truck should veer off course, the ignition can be interrupted.
5. fire-resistant suit, gloves, helmet, helmet liner, shoes, helmet restraints, kidney belt, neck collar
6. $140,000
7. How much time is put into detail and how many people are working on the project.

Bone Deep!: *(page 68)*

Before Reading:
1. The surgeon was the boy's mother.
2. Answers may vary. (e.g., wild animals, fires, drowning)
3. Answers may vary.
4. Answers may vary.

During Reading: From the man found in the back of the car; it might help determine what happened to the man and where.

After Reading:
1. No evidence to support either sex.
2. Answers may vary. (e.g., no one else to confer with; no crime lab)
3. Answers may vary.
4. *Solution:* The man cut himself with an axe while he and his wife were camping. The woman loaded him in the canoe and paddled frantically back to the landing where they had left their car. Once there she loaded her injured husband into the back of the car, and then realized she had forgotten the car keys back at their campsite. She then began walking to town to get help and was struck by a car on the way.

That's One Hanukkah of a Party: *(page 72)*

Before Reading:
1. Christmas – birth of Christ; Ramadan – feast month of Islam; Passover – Jewish celebration of deliverance from Egypt during time of Moses; Chinese New Year – celebrate new year on Chinese calender

2. Answers may vary.   3. They are part of the fabric that holds a society together giving people a common heritage.
4. Answers may vary. (e.g., so we can understand each other and live in peace)
5. Answers may vary. (e.g., becoming familiar with other cultures)

During Reading: Answers may vary.

After Reading:
1. Answers may vary.   2. candle holder with eight places   3. game device used for betting
4. Answers may vary.   5. Answers may vary.

The Hired Hand: *(page 76)*
Before Reading:
1. Answers may vary. (e.g., developing a sense of responsibility)
2. Answers may vary. (e.g., ties the family down when they want to go out of town)
3. Answers may vary. (e.g., yappy, excitable, short attention span)
4. Answers may vary.
5. characteristic – placid – tolerance – intent – vermin – absolute

During Reading: Answers may vary; She is beginning to like the idea of keeping the dog.

After Reading:
1. He felt they couldn't earn their keep around the farm.
2. She wanted Brady to find out how the terrier could be of use on the farm.
3. yappy, hyper
4. They were bred to hunt and kill vermin; had wiry coats; little tolerance of other animals.
5. if the dog could be taught to protect the chickens from vermin

Dealing With Failure: *(page 80)*
Before Reading:
1. Answers may vary.
2. It may not be as devastating because we are able to look back on how we survived an earlier similar experience.
3. Answers may vary. (e.g., perseverance)
4. Answers may vary.   5. Answers may vary.   6. Answers may vary.

During Reading: Answers may vary.

After Reading:
1. Answers may vary. (e.g., He was poor, had to work hard. He did not go to school regularly. His mother died. They moved.)
2. Lost his mother; woman he loved died; lost his job; worked hard when young; family moved; did not attend school regularly.
3. Answers may vary.
4. Answers may vary. (e.g., He accomplished so much despite a life of hardship and heartache. He was also successful as President during a very hard time.)
5. Thanksgiving   6. It took place during the American Civil War.

Skateboard Park: *(page 84)*
Before Reading:
1. Answers may vary. (e.g., coordination, balance, stamina)
2. Answers may vary.   3. Answers may vary. (e.g., variety of equipment)
4. Answers may vary.   5. a) movement; b) appearance; c) great; d) fan; e) depend;
   f) newcomer

During Reading: All skaters could enjoy the park without frustration at the equipment being too hard or too easy; Answers may vary.

After Reading:
1. It is much more satisfying if you don't have to keep stopping and starting.
2. Answers may vary. (e.g., ramps, smooth skating surface, grind rails, spines, quarter and half pipes, bleachers)
3. Answers may vary.   4. Answers may vary.
5. Answers may vary. (e.g., accomplishing goals, improving skills)

Girls are Taller: *(page 88)*
Before Reading:
1. Answers may vary.   2. Answers may vary. (e.g., reach puberty earlier)
3. boys are generally stronger, faster, etc.   4. a) ignorant   b) edgy   c) demand   d) infancy

During Reading: Answers may vary.

After Reading:
1. Answers may vary. (e.g., embarrassment)   2. Answers may vary. (e.g., outspoken, nerdy)
3. Their bodies are going through changes.   4. He showed them a picture.
5. time   6. Answers may vary.